Y0-CCS-388

SCOPE® Monograph on Aspects of acute inflammation

A. G. Macleod, M.D.

formerly of the Faculty,
University of Michigan School of Medicine;
Rockefeller University;
and consultant
to The Upjohn Company.

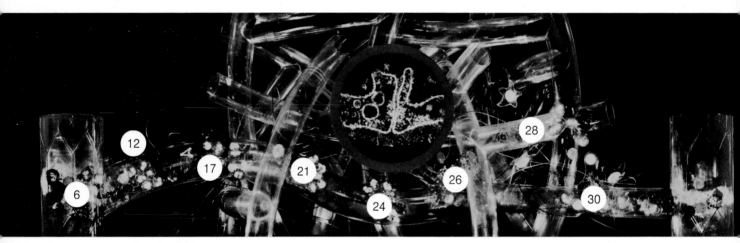

LIBRARY OF CONGRESS CARD NUMBER 78-112744

Reprinted 1975
Published by The Upjohn Company, Kalamazoo, Michigan
⊑ S-3251

Editor / Baird A. Thomas

Historical background

In the past The Upjohn Company has produced a number of exhibits with accompanying monographs featuring subjects of particular current interest in medical science. They have featured the discoveries made by the introduction of a revolutionary new research technique such as electron microscopy (The Cell), or an important new concept such as the structure of the DNA (desoxyribonucleic acid) molecule (Genes in Action). The subject featured in this year's exhibit and monograph, however, relies on neither a new technique nor an epoch-making discovery to give it interest but depends on its importance both to clinical medicine and biology in general. The subject is the organism's reaction to injury in defense of its existence—inflammation.

There have not been extraordinary, pivotal discoveries concerning inflammation in the past decade; only the conscientious application of every new device or method of approach to any aspect of the subject on which they might shed light. The exhibit and this booklet, therefore, celebrate no significant major scientific discovery, but hopefully will be a guide through a vast accumulation of discoveries which are more confusing than illuminating individually but of importance as an interrelated whole.

In any subject made up of so many small pieces, it is impossible to trace out the origin of each idea and give due credit for every contribution. Not only does the available space not allow it, but the reader would be led along so tortuous a path that he might well lose his way. Instead he will be guided along what currently seem the important paths.

Figure 1:
*Cornelius Celsus,
(approximately 30 B.C.-38 A.D.),
though probably not a physician, was the first
author to enunciate the four cardinal signs
of inflammation.*

The title of this essay implies that inflammation is primarily a defensive reaction which is important in restoring the organism to health following injury. As will be seen, it ordinarily is successful in eliminating or neutralizing the noxious agent and bringing about the repair of the damaged tissue. Thermodynamically, it is the means that the organism has for diverting a part of its energy and substance to repel a threat to its existence. It fails when more energy is required than can be supplied.

This concept of inflammation as a defense mechanism has not always been understood. The early physicians were familiar with the manifestations of inflammation. In fact, Celsus (1st Century A.D.) enumerated four of its cardinal signs: *tumor* (swelling), *rubor* (redness), *calor* (hotness) and *dolor* (pain), to which Galen (130-200 A.D.) added the fifth, *functio laesa* (loss of function). They and most of their successors, however, regarded it as simply a lesion, i.e., a manifestation of injury. It was perhaps John Hunter (1728-1793) who first recognized that inflammation was indeed a defense reaction. This idea was, of course, implied in the concept of laudable pus—a clinical indication that the body was winning the battle for recovery.

It was not until the development of histologic techniques and an understanding of normal microanatomy had been obtained that inflammation could be accurately described in cellular terms and rational theories developed as to its mechanism and purpose. This occurred largely during the last quarter of the 19th Century.

4

It is not possible here to delve deeply into the historical development of our present concepts of inflammation, but a little background will be helpful.

Rudolf Virchow (1821-1902) understood the histologic manifestations of inflammation and its recurrence with modifications in many pathologic situations. The theory he developed concerning its mechanism did not gain a wide acceptance. He believed that in some manner the body supplied the cells in the injured region with a superabundance of nutrition, and that in consequence they were increased in number and activity. This theory was too general, did not help in understanding many of the observable phenomena and lacked objective proof. It did, however, explain the local evolution of heat which subsequent theories have tended to neglect.

A considerable advance in understanding inflammation was made by S. Samuel and J. Cohnheim who focused attention on the small blood vessels. In fact Cohnheim believed that the entire process was explainable on the basis of the effect of injury on the vascular wall. It was his belief that some noxious material emanating from the site of injury weakens the vessel wall and causes it to leak both fluid and blood corpuscles. Subsequent work has indicated that this theory is certainly true so far as it goes, but there are also other aspects of inflammation which have to be considered, in particular the behavior of the white blood cells. Cohnheim like most of his predecessors regarded inflammation as a manifestation of injury and not an active defense reaction.

Another important phase to the investigation of inflammation was added by Elie Metchnikoff (1845-1916) before the close of the 19th Century. Metchnikoff was a zoologist and approached the subject from the standpoint of the evolution of the reaction to injury from its simplest manifestations in unicellular organisms to the complex process of inflammation in higher mammals. The protozoa, lacking for the most part tough or resistant cell walls to keep invaders out or organs usable for offense, must rely on their ability to destroy organisms by engulfing and digesting them and finally extruding the harmless debris. Since this is an active process, Metchnikoff emphasizes throughout his work on inflammation the idea of active defense against injury. As he progressively studies more and more complex organisms, he points out that with few exceptions each has cells which react actively to injury by attempting to

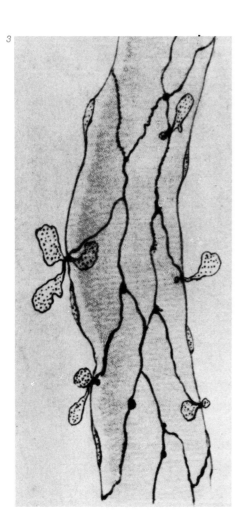

Figure 2:
Rudolf Virchow, (1821-1902),
was the great progenitor of cellular pathology,
stressing the idea that changes in disease
are due to fundamental alterations in the cell.

Figure 3:
Leucocytes emigrating from a small inflamed
vessel in frog mesentery
was observed by Julius Arnold in 1875
and reported in
Virchow's Archiv für pathologische Anatomie.

engulf and digest or simply to wall off the offending organism or object. It is of interest that in those organisms in which in the course of their development there is a mesoderm, the defending cells are derived from this.

In primitive organisms which do not have blood vessels, the defending cells make their way to the site of injury by amoeboid motion, and in some instances primitive connective tissue cells in the injured area take up the defense. When describing the reaction of mammals to injury, he describes the inflammatory process much as we understand it today but strongly emphasizes the role of the polymorphonuclear and mononuclear phagocytes, which he called microphages and macrophages respectively. But once again, inflammation has proved to be more than just phagocytosis. Much as Metchnikoff advanced the subject, he did its advancement a disservice in overemphasizing phagocytosis to the point that other aspects of the subject were neglected. He did, however, clearly indicate that inflammation is an active defense mechanism which is usually beneficial.

In the early part of the 20th Century there was a renewed interest in the microcirculation in connection with inflammation. A. Krogh made extensive studies of small blood vessels. He was particularly interested in their function in the exchange of metabolites. He showed that the number of capillaries carrying blood at any one time was subject to sensitive adjustment. In addition, Sir Thomas Lewis, in his later years, turned his attention from the heart to the microcirculation, inflammation, and its chemical mediators.

In the passing generation the great exponent of the study of inflammation was Valy Menkin. It is to him that we largely owe the modern concept of the process as a whole. He brought together the vascular reactions emphasized by Cohnheim, the phagocytic activities discovered by Metchnikoff, and the importance of the biochemical mediators and immune phenomena that are the principal subjects of research today. It was particularly his work on the humoral substances that trigger and govern the process that has been valuable. While the biochemical mediators Menkin described and named are no longer adequate to explain the accumulated experimental data, they pointed the direction which modern research is following. For many years Menkin kept alive interest in inflammation when few other investigators were concerned with it.

5

Figure 4:
Julius Cohnheim, (1839-1884),
in his studies on the pathology of inflammation,
pointed out the important part
played by the small blood vessels.
He emphasized that venules rather than capillaries
merited most attention.

Figure 5:
Elie Metchnikoff, (1845-1916),
demonstrated the nature of phagocytosis
as a defense mechanism that engulfed and
destroyed invading microorganisms.

Figure 6:
Valy Menkin, (1901-1960),
carried on persistent research into the cellular
nature of inflammation
at a time when few others were interested.
Although recent opinion considers his biochemical
work unsatisfactory, he was the first to suggest
polypeptides as mediators of inflammation.

Structure
of the
microcirculation

While it is no longer possible to believe as Cohnheim did that the entire process of inflammation is explainable on the basis of abnormalities of the small blood vessels, nevertheless, other than the initial injury itself, the earliest events in the inflammatory process involve the endothelium of the small venules. Consequently, an understanding of the anatomy of the microcirculation, i.e., the microvasculature, particularly the fine structure of the endothelial cells is essential.

The microcirculation *(Fig. 47, p. 44),* for the purpose of this discussion, is that through arterioles, venules and their intercommunications, the arteriovenous communications and the true capillaries. Even before Henryk Hoyer (1872) first visualized them it was realized that there are fairly direct communications between arterioles and venules and that many of the true capillaries arise from these channels. B. W. Zweifach believed that since many of these intercommunicating vessels have occasional smooth muscle fibers in their walls, often near capillary junctions, it is probable that neurogenic adjustment of the flow of blood through the shunts helps govern the flow through the capillaries, because it is generally agreed that so far as adjustment of blood flow is concerned, capillaries respond passively to the pressure gradient between their two ends.

As long ago as 1896, E. H. Starling's observations led him to conclude that water and other substances left the circulation through the fine cracks between the endothelial cells of the capillaries. On the other hand, R. Heidenhain even earlier had suggested that the endothelium might be actively secretory and not act as a passive porous membrane. As will be seen, these two opposing concepts in modern dress are still with us today.

In the 1950's, J. R. Pappenheimer and his associates made extensive studies of the diffusion of various substances from the circulation. They approached the subject from the physicochemical point of view with particular attention to the diffusion rates of molecules of different sizes. They employed both physiologic experiments and various types of models. It emerged that the rates of diffusion were roughly proportional to the molecular size. They concluded that their results were best explained by the assumption that a small percentage of the capillary surface consisted of cylindrical pores or narrow slits. If pores, their di-

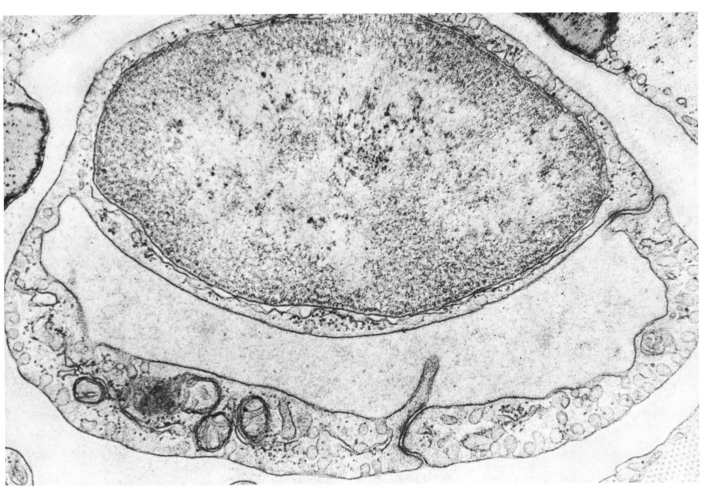

Figure 8:
The capillary in this electron micrograph displays two clearly demarcated endothelial cells and their junctions.
The nucleus of one is especially conspicuous.
An interesting feature, the function of which is not known, is the marginal fold—the long process visible at the junction at lower center.

ameter was about 30 Angstroms, and if slits, their width was about 37 Angstroms. Pappenheimer's studies have stood the test of time; consequently, the studies of morphologists directed toward locating the sites of transport of material from the capillary lumen to the tissue spaces must take them into account. Later work by G. Grotte indicated that in addition to the

8

pores postulated by Pappenheimer there were also sparsely distributed "leaks" (140 Angstroms) which passed much larger molecules.

In recent years the latest techniques of electron micrography have been utilized in depicting the fine structure of the endothelial cells and their junctions. Two other matters have also been considered by electron micrographers, the existence of an intercellular cement and an endocapillary layer both of which were hypothesized by R. Chambers and B. Zweifach from their extensive observations of the passage of blood through living capillaries.

Occasional cross sections of capillaries have been described in which there have been no junctions between cell processes. Usually, however, there are one or more junctions. In other words, the capillary is made up of a simple mosaic of flattened endothelium. Its diameter is small enough so that the cytoplasm of a single cell frequently extends completely around it. Scattered along this simple tube and closely applied to it are occasional cells, pericytes *(Fig. 9)*, whose function is still not clear, except perhaps in the retina of the eye where they are much more numerous and where they seem to have a supportive function for the endothelial cells.

Early electron micrographs of capillary endothelium indicated that these cells contain all the usual organelles found in tissue cells—mitochondria, endoplasmic reticulum, and Golgi complexes —and are bounded by the usual threelayered unit membrane. Nothing, however, corresponding to cylindrical pores was revealed, but it seemed possible that the cell junctions might be the hypothesized slits. But their width seemed in general too great for them to act like any kind of molecular sieve.

Close examination of the junctions has revealed some interesting features. Most conspicuous are the marginal folds which extend along the luminal aspect of the junctions, sometimes extending from one lip, sometimes from both *(Fig. 8)*. In cross section these, of course, appear like fingers. At high magnification the junctions are of considerable length, throughout most of which the components are a fair distance apart, but over one small segment they are closely approximated. *(Fig. 10)*. Since these tight junctions are visible in every section, it appears that there is a gasket extending completely along each of the junctions between cells. The character and consistency of these gaskets is obviously of great im-

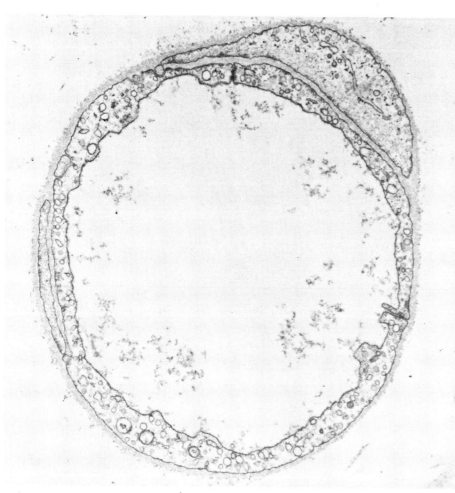

Figure 9:
A capillary, from mouse diaphragm,
shows two endothelial cells partially enfolded
by the processes of two pericytes
The basement membrane is clearly exhibited,
extending completely around the vessel
and the pericytes.

portance in understanding the transport of molecules of various sizes from the capillary lumen to the tissue spaces. In sections where the three layers of the unit membrane of the endothelial cells can be distinguished, it appears that the outermost layers from each component of the junction are fused at these tight junctions.

Another interesting feature of electron micrographs of endothelial cells is the vesicles which are most conspicuous along their luminal and external margins. That most of these vesicles open onto the cell surface is indicated by the fact that electron-opaque material injected either into the vessels or the tissue spaces can be observed in the vesicles on either the inner or outer surfaces respectively *(Fig.13)*. Some vesicles appear not to be connected to either surface. These

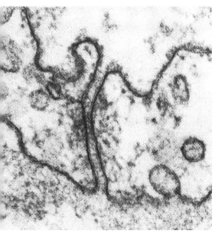

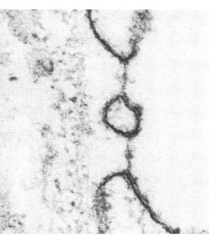

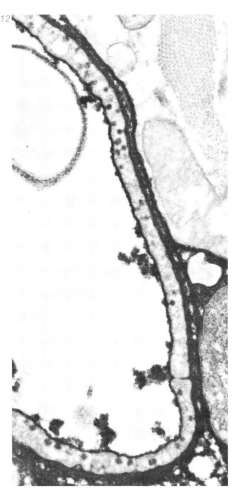

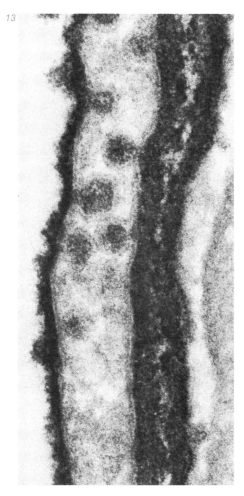

Figure 10:
normal endothelial junction,
s shown in this electron micrograph,
aries from about 200 Angstroms wide to about
40 Angstroms in the region known as
e "tight junction."

Figure 11:
his detail shows fenestrations in the endothelium
ridged by diaphragms that appear
be continuous with the outermost layer
the endothelial cell's unit membrane.

Figure 12:
A section of capillary from mouse diaphragm
treated with ruthenium red, which stains
mucopolysaccharides. The basement membrane
and an apparent endocapillary layer
are well labelled.

Figure 13:
Also labelled with ruthenium red
are vesicles or apparent invaginations
of the endothelium which are contiguous
to the basal and luminal borders.

observations have led to the idea that if these vesicles travel from one cell surface to the other, they might pick up fluid from the blood and transport it through the cell.

In suitably prepared specimens electron micrographs reveal a somewhat felt-like finely fibrillar layer surrounding the external surface of the capillary. This is the basement membrane which consist largely of collagen fibers. It has bee thought that this might act as a differen tial filter of material that had passed through the intercellular spaces. Mor recent studies make it seem unlikely tha much filtering is done by the basemen membrane except for large particles.

Electron microscopy is just as depend ent upon proper methods of fixation and staining as light microscopy, and con sequently, as these methods improved more and more of the fine structure o the cells has been revealed. Furthermore certain "staining" techniques which ma not be suitable for revealing the genera structure of cells may, however, be o great value in showing the presence of particular material and indicating wher in the cell it is located. An example o such a technique is the use of rutheniur red to demonstrate the presence of mu coproteins (mucopolysaccharides).

By the use of ruthenium red J. H. Lut has not only demonstrated the presenc of mucopolysaccharides in the basemer membrane of the endothelium in addi tion to the collagen fibers but the pres ence of a thinner layer of a similar mate rial lining the luminal surface of thes cells which probably represents the en docapillary layer described by Chamber and Zweifach (Fig. 12). It further ap pears that similar material is present i the junctions between the cells and migh constitute an intercellular cement.

Luft was also interested to see if th ruthenium red could penetrate the tigh junction between the endothelial cells. I at least one preparation where the dy was permitted to diffuse from the tissu spaces toward the lumen of the vessels it appeared to penetrate beyond the tigh junction and stain a small amount of ma terial on the luminal side of it (Fig. 14 While, because of technical difficultie not yet circumvented, unequivocal proc that these junctions can be penetrate by ruthenium red is still lacking, it seem ed likely to Luft that it is the mucoprotei material in these narrow isthmuses tha acts as the differential filter that is re sponsible for the molecular sieving de scribed by Pappenheimer. It is also o interest that estimates of the dimension of these tight junctions correspond roughly to those of the pores or slits pos tulated by Pappenheimer.

A still clearer demonstration that thes intercellular spaces can transmit mole cules of considerable size has been fur nished by M. J. Karnovsky. He used th enzyme horseradish peroxidase whic has a molecular weight of about 40,000

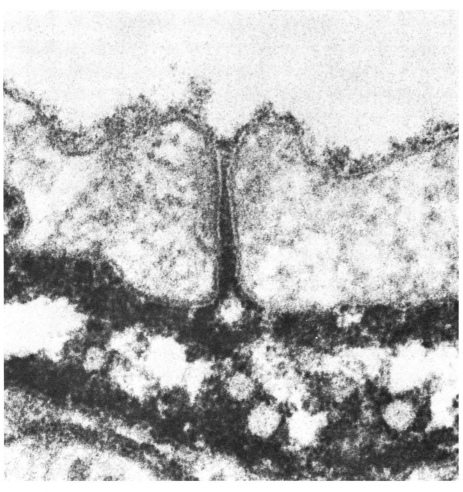

Figure 14:
The endothelial junction in this electron micrograph is filled, from the extravascular side, with material labelled by ruthenium red. It has penetrated through the "tight junction" and is diffusing along the luminal surface of the endothelium.

The presence of the enzyme can be detected in the electron micrograph by its ability to oxidize a heavy benzidine compound. The experiments of this author clearly show that this enzyme when introduced into the circulation can gain access to the tissue spaces via the intercellular junctions *(Fig. 15)* since it can be visualized actually in them.

In Karnovsky's pictures there is also staining of the intracellular vesicles, those opening on the luminal surface, some with no apparent contact with either surface, and those opening on the outer surface. Consequently, some material might well have been conveyed across the endothelial cytoplasm by this means. The author, however, regarded this as a slower and less important route. That material can indeed be conveyed across the capillary wall by way of these vesicles has been shown by G. E. Palade using ferritin particles. In his opinion this is the major means of transport because he believes that the intercellular junctions are for all practical purposes impermeable under normal circumstances and that the vesicular route is entirely adequate.

Up to this point we have been considering as typical the capillaries of skeletal muscle and, of course, these make up a very large part of the total capillary bed. It should be noted, however, that in certain tissues there are capillaries whose endothelial junctions are very different from those just described, notably endocrine glands, kidney and intestinal mucosa where there may be very large gaps between endothelial cells. For example, Fig. 11 shows the gap between two endothelial cells of a capillary of mouse intestine. While the gap itself is very wide, it is bridged by a thin membrane which Luft has indicated is probably of the same composition as and continuous with the outermost layer of the unit membrane of the endothelial cell. It would appear to be this diaphanous diaphragm that performs the sieving function in these special situations.

In summary, it appears that the electron microscopists have shown two possible means for substances to leave the capillaries and gain access to the tissue spaces. At the moment the intercellular spaces seem the most probable site of the small pores capable of molecular sieving and the vesicular transport probably accounts for the passage of large particles—the leaks of Grotte. Another possibility for the leaks is a large opening that may occur at the junction of several endothelial cells.

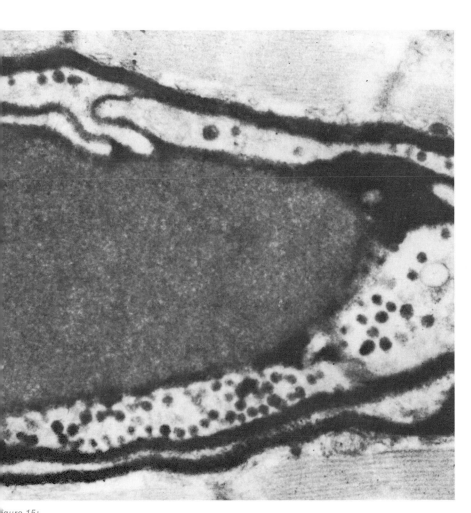

Figure 15:

orseradish peroxidase, used in this electron
icrograph, oxidizes a heavy benzidine
mpound and produces an electron dense
bstance (black). Here it has spread from the
men, through the endothelial junctions,
to the extravascular region. It has also
enetrated into many vesicles, implying that
ey are contiguous with the endothelial surfaces.

Initial events: Increased permeability

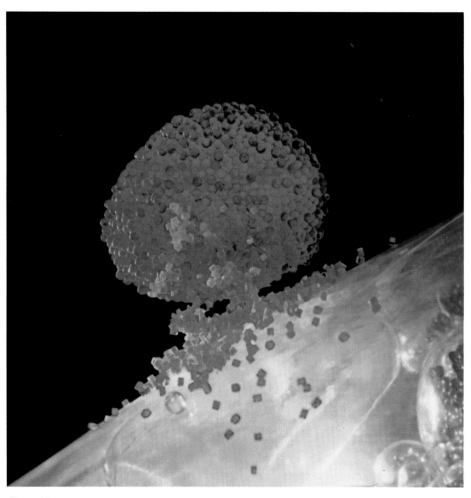

Figure 16:
*The model of a mast cell, near a blood vessel,
is shown discharging vasoactive substances (pink),
in reaction to an injury.
These substances, streaming toward the vessel
wall, may be among the mediators of
the inflammatory response.*

Acute inflammation

There are clearly two phases to the acut
inflammatory response, a brief early in
crease in vascular permeability of shor
duration and then, after a short interva
a much more prolonged second phas
consisting of the following events:

1 Increased permeability;

2 Sticking of white blood cells to th
vessel wall;

3 Diapedesis of white cells through th
wall, sometimes accompanied b
some red cells;

4 Accumulation of white cells in the in
jured area;

5 Phagocytosis of bacteria or other ma
terial by the white cells with the deat
of many of them;

6 Possible intensification of the reac
tion by materials released from th
white cells;

7 Leakage of fibrinogen and platelet
from the vessel;

8 Fibrin deposition in the area of injury

9 Intravascular clotting with destructio
of vessels;

10 Disposal by macrophages of most o
the necrotic debris;

11 Migration of fibroblasts and forma
tion of connective tissue;

12 Ingrowth of capillaries.

In time past the early phases of acute in
flammation were attributed to neurogeni
reactions influencing vascular flow in th
affected region. In most recent work
these phenomena are almost completel
neglected, although a recent paper b
J. H. Brown and associates has indicate
that the first phase of the acute inflamma
tory response does not occur in denerv

ated tissue. The reason for this neglect of the role of nerve impulses in inflammation is that more or less typical inflammatory reactions can be produced in tissue devoid of nerves.

Whatever the role of the nervous system, it has been recognized for a long time that mediation of most of the phenomena of inflammation must be humoral arising from some substance released by injury of tissue cells. It also seems likely that once the response is set in motion by the initial injury, subsequent events are linked to each other. The search for these chemical mediators has, however, been one of the most frustrating in modern biological science. There have been no clearcut breakthroughs, and each experiment seems to raise more questions than it answers.

Histamine

For many years histamine has attracted the attention of investigators who have in many ways tried to connect it with the inflammatory process. While histamine unquestionably has the ability to increase the permeability of small blood vessels, its action is very evanescent and it does not bring about conspicuous leucocyte sticking to the vessel wall. Current work seems to confirm, however, that it is probably largely responsible for the initial, transient phase of vascular permeability. This concept largely depends on the fact that this phase can be inhibited by antihistamines. Histamine may be released from mast cells *(Figs. 16, 17)*.

Vessels involved

While at one time it was thought that inflammation involved the capillaries, it is now clear that the process starts in the small venules and only later involves the true capillaries, spreading from the venous ends toward the arterioles. While this may be because of the delicacy and susceptibility of the endothelium of the venules, it also seems to have some relation to the venous nature of the blood itself, because if the flow of blood is reversed in the capillary by mechanically altering the pressure gradient, what was previously the arterial end of the vessel becomes the preferred site for inflammatory change (Zweifach).

This suggests that the fall in hydrostatic pressure from the arterial to the venous end of the small blood vessel renders the access of materials diffusing from the site of injury into the blood vessel easier at the low pressure end.

Although as has been indicated earlier there is considerable difference of opinion as to how fluid and solutes of various kinds leave the normal capillary, there is

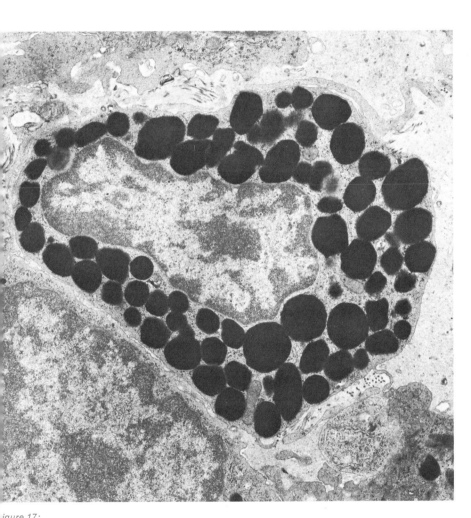

Figure 17:
An electron micrograph of a mast cell
in rat intestine shows the nucleus surrounded
by a cluster of conspicuous granules.
Mast cells are rich in mucopolysaccharides,
among which is heparin.
Bioactive amines and many enzymes are also
contained in mast cells and are probably
released from their granules.

14

no mystery as to how elements of the blood leave the permeable capillary in an inflamed area. The endothelial cells seem to round up, thereby pulling away from their attachments to each other and leaving sizable gaps through which both fluid and cells can escape *(Figs. 18-20)*.

Kinins

In considering the mediators of the delayed increase in permeability in acute inflammation it is as well to state at the beginning that no thoroughly satisfactory candidate has yet been found.

Years ago, Valy Menkin felt that the substance which he isolated from inflammatory exudate and called leukotaxin was this mediator. Current investigators have found that this extract is not a pure substance as Menkin believed it to be, but a mixture of various materials and that its activity is not due to the polypeptide which he believed to be the active substance but probably to other materials present in smaller amounts. Nevertheless, his work did call attention to the fact that the mediator was probably not a simple substance but a proteinaceous material of some molecular size and complexity. Current work seems to indicate that probably the mediators responsible for the increased permeability of blood vessels and for leucocyte sticking followed by emigration are separate and distinct substances and not a single substance as was at one time thought.

To date the most likely candidate for the mediator of the prolonged phase of the acute inflammatory process is a kinin. These substances are exceedingly potent inducers of increased permeability in venules and to a lesser extent in capillaries. While they are normally destroyed very rapidly in tissue by kininases, it is possible that they can be quite as rapidly released at the site of an acute inflammation. They are not nearly so potent at promoting the sticking of leucocytes and their subsequent migration through the vascular wall as they are at increasing permeability. It is now likely that these two manifestations of acute inflammation are mediated by different substances. Because there are no specific antagonists of the kinins, experiments similar to those done with antihistamines are not possible. There are, however, antagonists to the formation of kinins, and these substances are anti-inflammatory.

Kinins are polypeptides with powerful pharmacologic actions. They strongly affect the contraction of smooth muscle, produce hypotension, cause increased vascular permeability in small blood vessels, and induce severe pain when in-

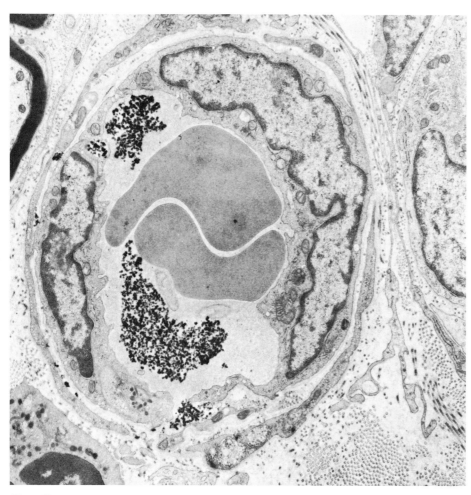

Figure 18:
Carbon particles, which have been injected into a capillary in an inflamed area of rat skin, may be seen in the lumen (in which are also two erythrocytes and two platelets).

Figure 19:
The permeability of the blood vessels,
an early phenomenon in the inflammatory process,
is the result of gaps formed at endothelial
junctions. Schematized in the model
is one of these gaps, caused by the "rounding-up"
of the cells.

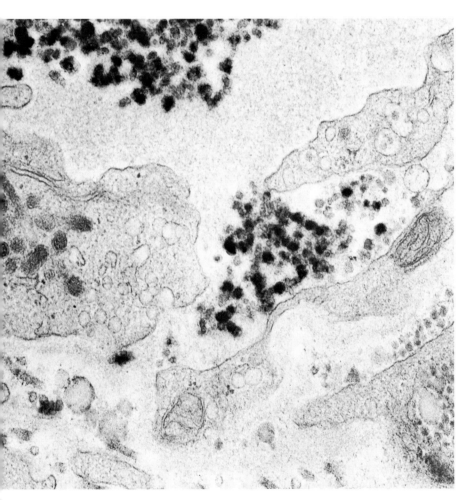

Figure 20:
detail from the lower portion of figure 18.
group of carbon particles has passed
rough a widely-open endothelial gap
nd is escaping into the perivascular area.

jected. Two of the best known ones, bradykinin and kallidin, are respectively a nonapeptide and a decapeptide. A number of others have been described and the generic name kinins is being used for the group.

The kinins do not exist as such in the blood but are generated under certain circumstances from one of the plasma globulins, kininogen. The generation of kinins involves three other interesting factors: Hageman factor, permeability factor/dil. and kallikrein.

Hageman factor is a plasma protein which when activated by contact with glass, other particulate matter or certain chemicals can set off a series of reactions leading to blood clotting. It was named for the first patient discovered who lacked the factor in his blood, Mr. John Hageman. Attention was called to the factor when it was discovered that Mr. Hageman's blood had a prolonged clotting time in a glass tube but that he had never shown any indication of a prolonged bleeding time.

Permeability factor-dilute is a protein originally discovered in guinea pig serum which causes localized increased vascular permeability when injected into the skin.

Kallikrein was discovered while investigating the hypotensive activity of urine. The name is derived from the Greek word for pancreas because that organ was found to contain large amounts of the substance. It is an enzyme.

The sequence in the formation of kinins is thought to be: Hageman factor is activated by contact with a suitable activator. This then converts pro-permeability factor-dilute to permeability

factor-dilute which in turn converts kalli-
kreinogen to kallikrein which finally produces kinin from kininogen. While the
proof that this is the series of reactions
that actually leads to the production of
kinin is still lacking, it is consistent with
what is known, and it is probable that
the actual one is similar.

Since the activation of Hageman factor which starts off the series of reactions
can occur in many ways including simple contact with glass or a foreign body,
it is the ideal triggering mechanism for
a reaction like inflammation that can
arise from so many causes.

Although the kinins have no specific
antagonists they are rapidly destroyed
by kininases. Their formation can also
be inhibited by agents that interfere with
the activation of Hageman factor, such
as hexadimethylene bromide, or that im-
pede other steps in kinin formation.
Anti-inflammatory corticosteroids appear
to prevent the kallikrein system from lib-
erating kinins.

Other mediators

The kinins are certainly good candidates
for the mediators of the increased permeability in the second phase of the
acute inflammatory response, but there
are others that need still to be considered. For one thing, kinins are not very
effective on true capillaries, and it has
been shown by R. S. Cotran and G. Majno
that heating the skin of animals to 54° for
20 seconds produced a reaction in which
the principal increase in permeability was
in the capillaries. In their hands, lyso-
lecithin, a new candidate as a mediator
in inflammatory reactions particularly
those involving antigen-antibody reactions, produced a similar result.

It appears that the mediators involved
in the immune type of inflammation are
probably different than those involved in
other types of inflammation. In the type
of inflammation caused by circulating
antibody such as urticaria, histamine may
be relatively more important than in other
varieties as evidenced by the greater efficacy of antihistamines in this kind of
lesion.

In the delayed type of hypersensitivity,
it appears that none of the mediators dis-
cussed so far is involved. In this chronic
type of inflammation, two mediators that
have been considered are RNA (ribonu-
cleic acid) and a material extracted from
lymph node cells called lymph node permeability factor (LNPF). This latter factor
is particularly interesting since it has very
little activity except to increase the permeability of the small blood vessels. Its
activity is reduced by salicylate.

Figure 21:
In addition to the appearance of endothelial gaps,
the "sticking" of leucocytes and platelets
is one of the first observable events to take place
as the organism responds to insult.
White cells and platelets begin to stick
to the endothelial wall and to each other,
but red cells continue to flow
in the central zone of the lumen.

Sticking and emigration of leucocytes

Figure 22:
This section of the model
shows polymorphs emigrating from the vessel,
ameboid fashion, through opened junctions
in the endothelial wall.
At lower center a neutrophil has reshaped itself
after emerging from the blood vessel.

One of the most striking phenomena observable in living blood vessels in the early stages of acute inflammation is that the white blood cells cease to float freely in the blood stream keeping pace with the red cells as they pass along the venules but adhere closely to the endothelium. Furthermore, the leucocytes not only stick to the endothelium but also to each other. All the granulocytic cells are involved—particularly the polymorphonuclears and also the monocytes, and platelets (Figs. 21, 23). The small lymphocytes are the notable exceptions.

Since there is increased permeability to plasma proteins where sticking is not observed and in other vessels sticking where there is no evidence of increased permeability to colloids, these two processes seem to be brought about by different mediators.

Sticking and phagocytosis

Whatever the mechanism of sticking, the phenomenon seems in some way to be associated with phagocytosis. For example, if leucocytes are allowed to phagocytize pneumococci *in vitro*, they stick to each other and form tightly adherent clumps. F. Allison and M. G. Lancaster have studied this phenomenon using both rabbit and human white cells. They found that if the medium was deionized by various means, both phenomena were inhibited. But they could be restored by the addition of either calcium or magnesium ions. Of the two, magnesium was the more effective. Since both Ca^{++} and Mg^{++} were divalent, they tested the efficacy of other divalent cations and found that both manganese and nickel were very potent for this purpose. Cadmium and lead were moderately effective and

18

so was trivalent iron. Divalent iron an
other monovalent and trivalent meta
had little activity. The fact that other diva
lent ions were as effective as calcium c
more so seemed to rule out any clos
relationship to fibrin formation.

The possibility of the participation c
an enzyme in this phenomenon was als
considered, and the effect of various er
zymes and enzyme inhibitors was triec
Because both phagocytosis and clump
ing were almost completely inhibited b
epsilon-amino-caproic acid, a known ir
hibitor of proteolytic enzymes, and fc
other reasons, Allison and Lancaster fe
that possibly a proteolytic enzyme wa
involved. Such an enzyme might act on
protein that in some way alters the ce
surface.

The behavior of both rabbit and huma
leucocytes was essentially the same. Th
experimental procedures usually affecte
phagocytosis and clumping of leucocyte
equally, but there were some slight di
ferences so that the processes thoug
closely related may not be identica
Since leucocytes tend to stick to eac
other as well as to the endothelial cell:
it is probable that whatever causes th
phenomenon acts on both types of cell:

Emigration

Very soon after sticking is observed, th
leucocytes are seen to work their wa
through the endothelium and perivascu
lar structures into the tissue space:
Electron micrographic studies indica
that this is accomplished by their insinu
ating a pseudopod into an intercellula
junction of the endothelial cells, enlargir
this opening somewhat and eventual
squeezing through it *(Figs. 22, 24, 25*
Only granulocytes and monocytes ac
tively work their way out of the vesse
but it would appear that a few red cel
and lymphocytes may take advantage c
the holes they create and emerge with
out any preliminary sticking *(Fig. 26)*.

Mediators of emigration

While substances known to promote vas
cular permeability often occasion som
emigration of leucocytes, the respons
is usually delayed and weak. A grea
many substances produce such re
sponses, for example, plasma. It is pos
sible that any agent producing vascula
permeability might cause mild delaye
emigration of leucocytes because of th
extravasated plasma.

Extracts of burned skin, J. V. Hurle
found, produced a prompt and very ir
tense emigration of leucocytes. This i
the type of response that would be ex
pected from a specific mediator of th
phenomenon. It was also found that leu

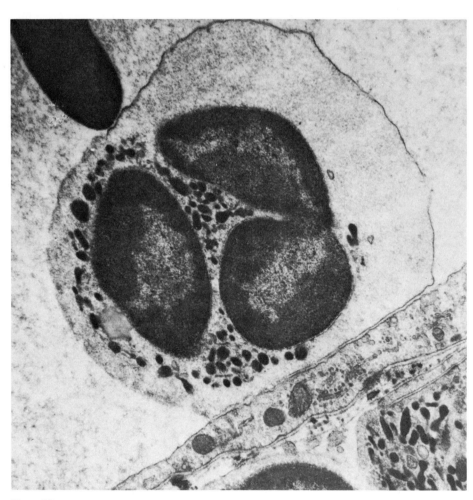

Figure 23:
*An electron micrograph of a sticking polymorph
shows the plasma membrane of the polymorph
flattened against the luminal surfaces
of two endothelial cells, whose junction it covers.
The very narrow space between the blood cell
and the endothelial wall may be an artifact.*

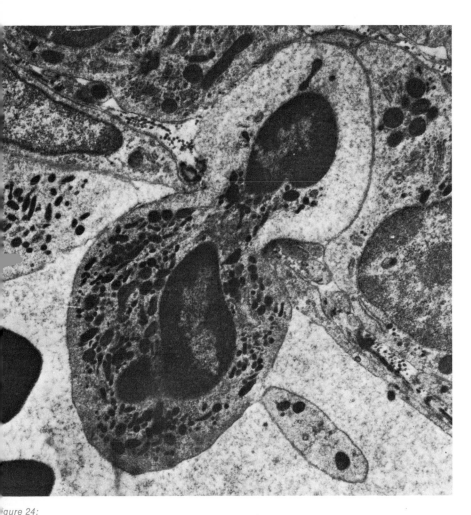

Figure 24:
A neutrophil, in this electron micrograph,
is passing through an endothelial gap.
As the leading edge advances it is notably empty
of granules, which will flow back into it later on.
In the lumen a platelet adheres to the neutrophil
and a portion of a second neutrophil
may be glimpsed, adhering to the first one
and to the endothelium.

cocytes extracted with saline produced an intense migration of leucocytes. To ascertain whether or not it was the leucocytes in the burned skin that produced the response, rats were treated with nitrogen mustard to the point that they were devoid of leucocytes and burned. An extract of their burned skin was made and tested. It produced an intense response even though the skin was almost devoid of white cells. The inciting material was then sought in serum, but serum by itself produced little response. When, however, serum was incubated with white cells or minced tissue of various kinds, potent materials were produced. The active substance was nondialyzable, stable when heated to 60°C for 30 minutes, but destroyed if kept at this temperature for one hour. It was destroyed by trypsin. Its action was not prevented by the prior administration of antihistamines, amine oxidase inhibitors, quinine or salicylate.

It was hypothesized that some factor in serum was acted on by a substance present in injured tissue; this factor would then produce the active mediator of leucocyte emigration.

To test the possible relation between chemotaxis and leucocyte emigration, the various extracts were tested for chemotatic activity in a modified Boyden chamber, and it was found that their ability to induce emigration of leucocytes and their chemotactic activity were parallel. It appears, therefore, that there is an endogenous material that can be produced by injury that is capable of inducing migration of leucocytes and possibly attracting them to the site of injury.

There is obviously a relationship between sticking of leucocytes, their emigration, chemotaxis and phagocytosis since, in a sense, they are all stages in the process that gets the phagocytic cells to the material to be phagocytized. It would not be surprising therefore if the same substance mediated more than one of these stages.

Whether or not this material described by Hurley is also the substance responsible for the preliminary sticking of the white cells to the endothelium and each other and also probably involved in phagocytosis remains to be shown.

A complex of three components of complement C_5, C_6, and C_7 seems to be highly chemotactic for polymorphonuclear neutrophils and eosinophils, particularly when it has been fixed in an antigen-antibody reaction. Mononuclears are also attracted by components of complement but different ones from those attracting granulocytes.

Chemotaxis

While a straight forward enough phenomenon *in vitro,* chemotaxis has not been satisfactorily demonstrated *in vivo.* In fact, Sumner Wood, Jr. using a cinematographic method has plotted in detail the peregrinations of a single polymorphonuclear leucocyte. The movements were active but there was no indication that it had any tendency to move toward an area of injury or a highly chemotactic substance. It moved quite as often away from as toward the chemotactic material. Why the highly chemotactic materials failed to attract the polymorphs *in vivo* remains to be explained.

Most tests made for chemotaxis in recent years have been made in the Boyden chamber, two shallow compartments separated by a millipore filter. The chemotactic substance is placed in one compartment and leucocytes in the other. The pores of the filter are so small that leucocytes can only get through by ameboid movement. In so confined a space, chance alone would bring many cells to the membrane. Perhaps only there does the attractant stimulate the cell to penetrate it. In other words, the attraction of the chemotactic substance might actually act only over a very short distance. Consequently, the demonstration of chemotaxis by this means does not necessitate that the leucocyte be able to follow a concentration gradient toward the substance for any great distance, but rather that coming close to it by chance it remains and attempts to engulf it.

Lymphocytes

One cell that is always present in a normal inflammatory exudate and which arrives there fairly early in the course of the process is the lymphocyte. This cell has not been observed by the electronmicroscopists to leave normal small blood vessels via the intercellular junctions unless it is washed through a hole left by a polymorph or monocyte. It has, however, been seen to leave the vessels in lymph nodes by piercing the endothelial cytoplasm. Furthermore, according to the work of A. R. Page the substances that induce the emigration of leucocytes do not induce the emigration of lymphocytes; an entirely different mediator seems involved. In the first place, a prior emigration of neutrophils seems to be required, because in neutropenic animals the lymphocyte response is either prevented or greatly delayed. Apparently this agent is an inducer of new protein synthesis in the lymphocyte, since the response is prevented by drugs that interfere with protein synthesis.

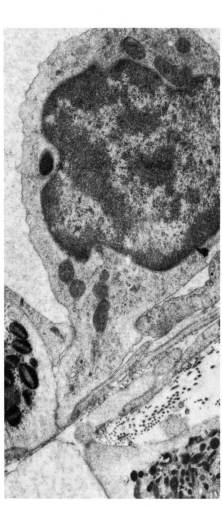

Figure 25:
A monocyte is beginning the journey through an endothelial gap by pushing a pseudopod into the opening. At right, an eosinophil, already outside the vessel, partially blocks the emerging monocyte.

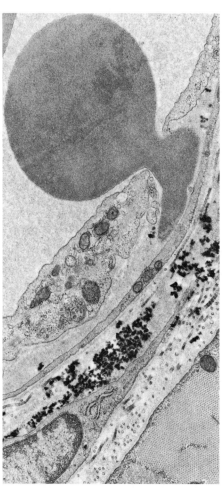

Figure 26:
Erythrocytes are passive cells. Here an erythrocyte has probably been washed into an already existing endothelial gap and because of its extreme plasticity it will be squeezed through it.

Phagocytosis by leucocytes

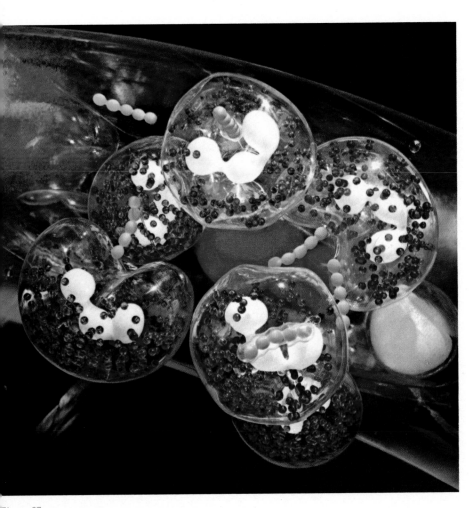

Figure 27:
Phagocytosis appears to be the main business
of emigrated leucocytes.
In the model a population of invading bacteria
(green) is being swallowed up by a group
of neutrophils in the extravascular space.
Various stages of phagocytosis are demonstrated
here, some of which are shown separately
on the following pages.

Once the granulocytes and macrophages have arrived at the site of injury, they start the removal of the irritating materials and also the remnants of injured tissue. They do this by engulfing the particulate matter which they then attempt to destroy enzymatically. The importance of phagocytosis was particularly emphasized by Metchnikoff. He observed that the process is a very general one and is utilized by animals of all stages of evolution. It, however, reaches its greatest development in mammals. In the lowest forms, it is indistinguishable from the process whereby the creature obtains its nutrition, but in higher forms it is a specialized defense reaction. Metchnikoff called attention to two types of cells in higher mammals involved in this process, the microphages and macrophages. His microphages are the neutrophils which are the first phagocytes to leave the blood stream and arrive at the site of injury. His macrophages we still call macrophages, the large phagocytic mononuclears.

There is no doubt that phagocytosis is a very important means of protection. So strong a case did Metchnikoff make for the importance of phagocytosis that a whole generation regarded it the most important if not the sole defense mechanism of the body to the neglect of some of the other factors in natural resistance to disease.

Early in the study of phagocytosis it was discovered that not all the bacteria and particles were engulfed with equal ease. In the case of bacteria, there was a relationship between the ease with which they were phagocytized and their virulence. Bacteria that might be capable of

22

vigorous reproduction were of little path ologic consequence if they were readily phagocytized, for it is possible for these body cells to dispose of surprisingly large numbers of invaders in a very short time —faster than they can reproduce. However, organisms that were disposed of more slowly were the dangerous invaders. Sometimes protective capsules interfered with phagocytosis. These had to be in some way attacked or disposed of before the leucocytes could engulf the invaders.

Rather obviously the ability of a leucocyte to engulf an organism depends on the relationship of the surface of the organism and that of the leucocyte. A relationship has already been mentioned between phagocytosis and the sticking of leucocytes to each other. A closely related phenomenon has been observed when bacteria are injected intravascularly. The leucocytes engulf them but are simultaneously observed to stick to the endothelial wall and to each other.

Opsonins

Of great practical importance in the process of phagocytosis is a group of antibodies formerly known as opsonins and now classified among the cytophilic antibodies. These antibodies in lieu of reacting with antigen become attached to the surface of the bacteria and make it much easier for the leucocytes to attack them. Certain factors of complement seem also involved in rendering the bacteria attractive to white cells. Since time is required for these antibodies to develop, they are of greater importance in the later stages of inflammation than in the earlier.

Polymorphs

Mature polymorphonuclear leucocytes like red cells are end cells; that is, they are incapable of reproduction and even of repairing and restoring themselves. The endoplasmic reticulum that they possessed during their developmental stages has greatly decreased in amount in the mature cell. When their granules are fully formed, the evidence of protein synthesis within the cell has largely ceased. Elongation and lobulation of the nucleus occurs at maturity and probably is an indication of nuclear inactivity or deterioration. There is no evidence of DNA synthesis.

Polymorphs are formed in very large numbers in the bone marrow. In a mature man 20 to 30 billion circulate in the blood. Almost an equal number are caught in closed down capillaries, are adherent to vessel walls or are otherwise immobilized. In addition, there are prob-

Figure 28:
An early stage of phagocytosis:
In the model, a schematized neutrophil
is forming pseudopods
as it approaches a chain of cocci and prepares
to engulf them.

ably more than fifty times as many mature leucocytes in reserve in the bone marrow as are circulating in the blood at any one time.

The polymorph has an active carbohydrate metabolism and stores glycogen which it uses as a reserve source of energy. The many fine granules seen scattered throughout the cytoplasm are stored glycogen. During phagocytosis the carbohydrate metabolism increases, indicating that the process is an active one requiring energy and not a passive one as was at one time believed.

The polymorphs are also capable of metabolizing fat. While they are capable of aerobic metabolism ending in carbon dioxide, they are also capable of anaerobic glycolysis yielding lactic acid. This latter process is perhaps the preferred one. It has the advantage of making it possible for the cell to carry on its phagocytic activity when the circulation is impaired or in areas of necrosis. Probably the lactic acid from the polymorphs contributes to the acidity of old exudates.

Ordinarily the polymorphonuclear neutrophils are the first cells to emigrate from the blood vessel and proceed toward the inflamed area. They seem to be particularly concerned with the phagocytosis of bacteria. They are short-lived and incapable of cell division, so that they have to be continually supplied as needed from the blood stream. What the feedback mechanism is that triggers the release of leucocytes from the bone marrow when the numbers in the circulating blood are reduced is not known. Whatever this mechanism may be, it is very efficient at maintaining the white cell level in the blood constant under normal circumstances and elevating it when necessary.

Macrophages

Although the large mononuclears or macrophages arrive at the site of inflammation somewhat later than the polymorphs, it appears that they start to emigrate at about the same time. They, however, move somewhat slower. They are much longer-lived than the polymorphs and are capable of cell division. Although they are seldom observed in the process of mitosis, studies using labels of various sorts indicate that after the early stages a large proportion of the macrophages at the site of inflammation is derived from cell division. Many are also supplied from continued emigration. The macrophages are much more efficient than the polymorphs at phagocytizing fibrin and cellular debris from the site of inflammation in preparation for repair.

Figure 29:
The cocci are in process of envelopment by the neutrophil and only a fraction of the chain is still outside the blood cell.

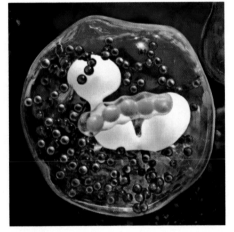

Figure 30:
The chain, now inside the neutrophil, is enclosed in a pouch formed by an invaginated section of the blood cell's plasma membrane.

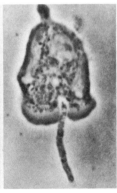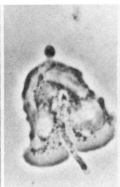

Figure 31:
Four remarkable frames from a phase contrast motion picture in which a human neutrophil phagocytizes a Bacillus megaterium.

Lysosomal activity

Figure 32:
The granules of the polymorphs
(purple in the model)
are lysosomes, organelles that contain a variety
of digestive enzymes.
Some of these granules attach themselves
to the pouch in which the ingested bacteria
are encased.

Leucocytic disposal of phagocytized material involves a new organelle, the lysosome, discovered by Christian de Duve a little over a decade ago. They are observable in electron micrographs of cells as membrane-lined sacs or vesicles of various sizes. According to de Duve, to qualify as a lysosome these vesicles should contain hydrolytic enzymes.

Stains indicating the presence of acid phosphatase are often used to identify lysosomes both by light and electron microscopy. Lysosomes can be identifed in many if not most kinds of cells. In connection with inflammation, we are particularly concerned with the lysosomes of polymorphs and macrophages.

Lysosomes may be thought of as protective storage containers filled with preformed substances required for various purposes. Gerald Weissmann has listed 31 substances found in lysosomes. Not all of these substances are enzymes and not all of them are found in every lysosome. Many of them would be inimical to the welfare of the cell were they free in the cytoplasm. Consequently, the important function of the lysosomal membrane is to keep them walled off until they are required for disposing of the phagocytized material or for other purposes.

This membrane is sometimes three-layered like the unit membrane of the cell and sometimes seems to have but one layer. Its composition, however, is similar to the plasma membrane's.

The contents of lysosomes being largely protein are probably formed in the endoplasmic reticulum and then transferred to the Golgi complex for concentration. How Golgi vesicles containing this material—sometimes called prolysosomes—coalesce into lysosomes is not clear. The granules of neutrophils are good examples of preformed lysosomes, formed as the cell develops. By the time the cell is mature, it has lost its ability to synthesize protein and new lysosomes cannot be formed. In macrophages, however, many of their lysosomes develop after they have left the blood vessels and reached the seat of injury.

In phagocytosis, what happens is this: The cell engulfs a bacterium or particle by developing an invagination of the plasma membrane which closes around the particle *(Figs. 27-31),* producing a closed sac, (which in a protozoan would be a "food vacuole"), in current parlance called a phagosome. This phagosome becomes detached and moves into the interior of the cell where it contacts and subsequently unites with one or more preformed lysosomes to become a phagolysosome.

Phagosomes have also been observed to unite with small Golgi vesicles, the prolysosomes, on their passage toward the center of the cell.

If it is a living bacterium that has been phagocytized, it may remain alive until contact with the lysosome. It is apparently not the hydrolytic enzymes that kill the bacterium; there are special substances that perform the *coup de grace.* In the list of substances in lysosomes, there are some nonenzymatic basic proteins which are bactericidal, notably phagocytin.

The method of engulfing avoids bringing the phagocytized material into direct contact with the cytoplasm and brings it into the cell surrounded by a membrane similar to that of the lysosome. Consequently, when the two come in contact it is possible for them to fuse, forming the phagolysosome. The contents of the lysosome are thus spilled into the phagosome without coming in contact with the cell substance. The enzymes can then act upon the ingested material without interfering with the cell's functioning.

J. G. Hirsch's movies show that when a bacterium is engulfed, the lysosomes begin to disappear and if a number of bacteria are ingested, the cytoplasm of the phagocytes becomes almost clear.

Electron micrographic studies by D. Zucker-Franklin and J. G. Hirsch clearly show how the membranes of the phagosome and the lysosome fuse on making contact so that the membrane of the phagosome and the lysosome become continuous. They also show that numerous lysosomes contribute their contents to the digestive vacuole. *(Figs. 33, 34).*

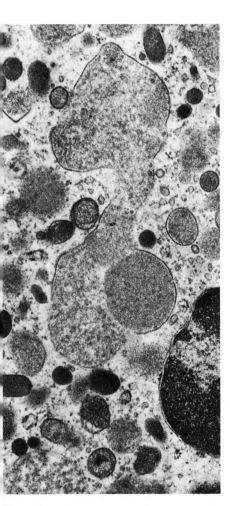

Figure 33:
Cytoplasm of a polymorph with many lysosomes. One of these is seen joined to the sac in which a phagocytized substance (in this case rheumatoid factor complex) is contained. The membrane of the lysosome has become continuous with that of the phagosome.

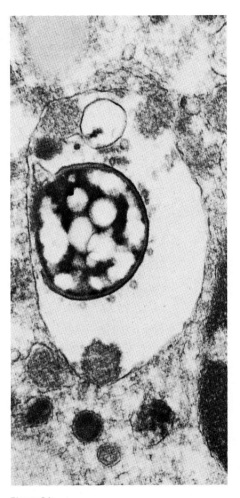

Figure 34:
The pouch in which a bacterium is trapped has fused with three lysosomes, becoming a secondary lysosome, or phagolysosome. The enzymatic contents of the primary lysosome and their intended prey, the bacterium, are now in a common container.

Enzymes and tissue destruction

Figure 35:
*In some cases the enzymes normally contained
in the lysosomes may continue their proteolytic
action after performing their phagocytic function.
In this photograph of the model, hydrolases,
released from lysosomes of a disrupted blood cell
are escaping into the tissue
where they may cause further damage.*

The enzymes from the lysosomes are capable of breaking down and solubilizing protein and carbohydrate but have little effect on lipids, so there is usually a certain amount of undigested material left in the phagolysosome which is now called a residual body.

J. T. Dingle has pointed out the importance of the membranous structures involved. He feels that they have significance in this and similar processes, and that physical and chemical studies of them may prove of importance. As he pointed out, substances that are capable of influencing lysosomal activity are often surface active, such as vitamin A.

The studies on hypervitaminosis A have been valuable for the understanding of the function of lysosomes. It was observed that the destruction of cartilage in this condition was very similar to what happens when a proteolytic enzyme like papain is injected intravenously. Close observation at the cellular level revealed that in the case of overdosage with vitamin A, proteolytic enzymes were released from the lysosomes of the cartilage cells which attacked the matrix of the tissue. It seems probable that the vitamin gained access to the lysosomal membranes and reduced their stability. The cartilage cells did not appear to be injured and when the vitamin was withdrawn the cartilage regenerated. Weissmann has called attention to the possibility that the resorption of the tadpole's tail is a similar process, and was, in fact, able to bring this about prematurely by administering vitamin A.

It has been demonstrated that lysosomes are also involved when cells destroy part of their own substance under

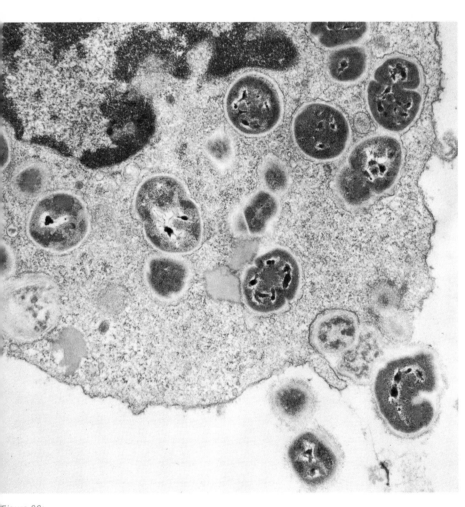

Figure 36:
*A mononuclear phagocyte, or macrophage,
which has ingested many streptococci,
and (before fixation) was about to phagocytize
the coccus at the lower right
in this electron micrograph.*

conditions of anoxia or metabolic stress. When this occurs, part of the cell substance becomes enclosed in a membrane similar to a phagosome's and is called an autolysosome. When such a vacuole has fused with one or more lysosomes, the cellular fragment is digested in the same way as any other phagocytized material.

So far, much of what has been said about lysosomes has concerned those of neutrophils, but phagocytosis is much the same in macrophages except that much of their lysosomal material seems to be generated after they emerge from the blood vessels *(Fig. 36)*. As they approach the injured area, they undergo both a functional and structural change and greatly increase their activity. Unlike the neutrophils, they are not end cells.

There is no doubt that the contents of lysosomes are capable of tissue injury and destruction. Consequently, it has been hypothesized that the escape of these substances from the phagolysosome into the cell substance accounts for the disintegration of the neutrophils with the release of substances capable of intensifying and perpetuating the inflammatory response. This hypothesis is attractive. The evidence advanced for it however, is indirect and the case remains to be proved.

In certain species a factor in neutrophils, when released, is capable of degranulating mast cells and thus possibly intensifying the inflammatory response. This factor, however, cannot be released from rat or human polymorphs.

Some of the most convincing evidence for the tissue-damaging potential of lysosomes comes from experiments on the localized Shwartzman reaction. This phenomenon consists of a hemorrhagic and necrotizing reaction at the site of a local injection of endotoxin when an intravenous dose of the same endotoxin is given 24 hours later. The reaction has been shown to be dependent upon the accumulation of leucocytes at the site because it does not occur in animals made agranulocytic by nitrogen mustard or other means. If, however, in such an animal lysosomes from neutrophils are injected at the site of the sensitizing injection prior to giving the challenging dose of endotoxin, a typical reaction occurs. These experiments are consistent with the idea that the outpouring of the white cell lysosomes causes the reaction and that they are involved whether or not they are in white cells. Unequivocal proof that this is indeed the pathogenesis of the reaction is, however, still lacking.

Vascular occlusion and deterioration

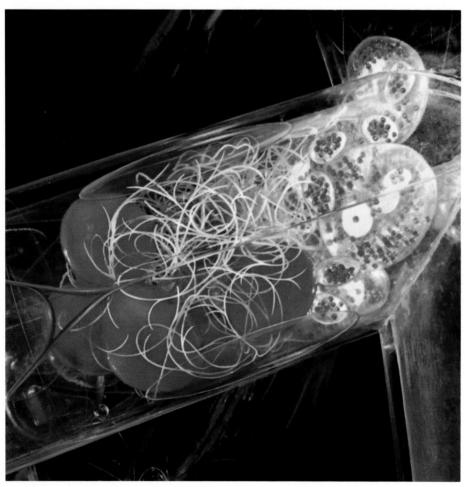

Figure 37:
In the model platelets and leucocytes,
stuck to the vessel wall, are forming a thrombus.
Strands of fibrin form and other cells,
erythrocytes, more platelets and leucocytes,
become entrapped.
The vessel is effectively blockaded
and blood is shunted off into other channels.

When small vessels are cut or injured, there are in general three types of plugging that may occur: the formation of fibrin, the aggregation of platelets, and combinations of the two. Observation of living vessels clearly shows the formation of all these types of obstruction.

In inflammation the original insult may actually damage vessels mechanically or various abnormal chemical substances resulting from the insult may stimulate plugging directly or indirectly by their influence on permeability, etc.

Fibrin formation

Any adequate discussion of the various factors influencing fibrin formation would require more space than is available here. In an inflammatory process of any extent, conditions in the tissue leading to the activation of Hageman factor (factor XII) are always present. As has been pointed out elsewhere, the activation of this factor is probably involved in the production of kinins which have a role in bringing about the permeability of venules. Any conditions which activate this factor for one purpose would make it available for another. This would apply particularly to the clotting of plasma extravasated into the tissues. However, as the process progresses and the tissue becomes edematous, the circulation slows and conditions favorable to fibrin formation occur inside the vessel as well as outside it.

As has been mentioned, one of the important factors in blood clotting is probably involved in inflammation. Since there are connections other than Hageman factor between blood clotting and inflammation, and since the latter process is almost always accompanied by the former, some authors feel that fibrin formation is importantly involved in inflammation. N. Jansco has brought forth considerable evidence in support of this idea. He finds, for example, that many chemical agents are both anticoagulant and anti-inflammatory.

Platelet aggregation

In small vessels platelet aggregation is quite as important as fibrin formation in forming plugs. While under conditions leading to the sticking of leucocytes, platelets adhering to the vessel wall can often be seen, the two phenomena seem to be separate, because either can occur without a conspicuous degree of the other. Platelets, singly or in clumps, may be observed sticking to an area of injury in a vessel wall shortly after the injury has occurred. The first clumps to form may be quite small and after a time pull away and wash down stream and either break up or form small emboli. Eventually a clump becomes firmly adherent to the vessel wall. Then platelets keep accumulating until a solid plug is produced. In the early loose aggregates the platelets retain their fine structure and their plasma membranes intact (Fig. 38). As the aggregate grows, the fine structure of the platelets, notably the granules, disappear, and the outlines of the individuals become indistinct. In these older solid plugs there is usually a considerable admixture of fibrin with the platelets. Such plugs do not wash away.

What the change is in the endothelial and platelet surfaces that makes sticking possible is not known. However, there are indications that ADP and certain vasoactive amines may be involved.

In addition to platelet aggregations forming plugs for small vessels, these structures contribute a factor which promotes fibrin formation. Before the complex nature of fibrin formation was understood, platelets were thought to be one of the principal sources of thromboplastin and were often referred to as thrombocytes.

Extravascular clotting

Extravascular clotting of plasma occurs in almost all forms of acute inflammation and in wounds acts as a cement to hold the edges of the disrupted tissue together. It also fills any gap which may exist. Much of the inflammatory exudate may become entangled in such a clot. A certain amount of endovascular clotting is also almost inevitable. If the reaction is severe, most of these plugged vessels disintegrate, partly as a result of anoxia and partly because of noxious materials emanating from the site of injury.

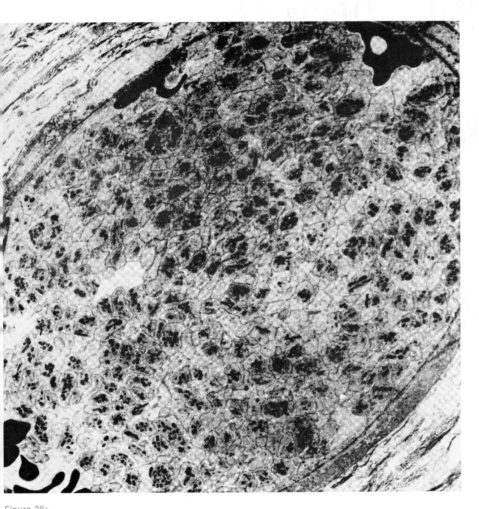

Figure 38:
A thrombus formation in an arteriole
in a hamster cheek pouch.
Aggregated platelets almost fill the lumen.
The platelet outlines are distinct, indicating
an early stage of aggregation.
Within an hour of the formation of the plug
the mass begins to become amorphous.

Repair
of
injury

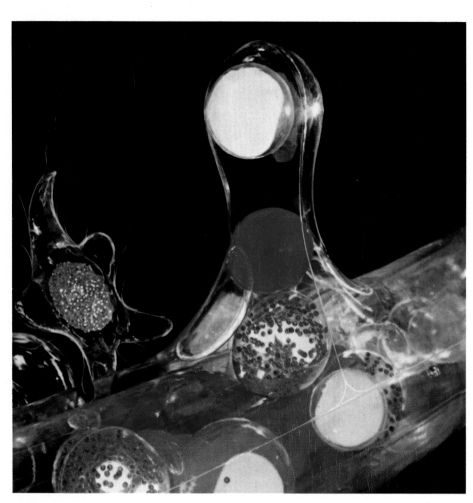

Figure 39:
*In healing tissues new vessels grow out
of viable existing ones.
A budding capillary appears in the model
in a regenerating area.
In the background a star-shaped fibroblast
synthesizes tropocollagen, which will contribute
to the building-up of strands
of connective tissue.*

The repair of any inflammatory lesion closely resembles the healing of a wound unless the lesion has been so small and inconsequential that no appreciable amount of tissue has been destroyed. Since in mammals true regeneration is possible in very few tissues (liver, epithelia and blood), healing is much the same in all situations and consists of replacing what has been destroyed with fibrous connective tissue.

Once the cause of the inflammation has been removed or destroyed by phagocytosis or other means, repair can commence. Ordinarily it is the normal sequel to inflammation. As indicated in the previous section, many of the blood vessels in the inflamed area have been destroyed. Consequently it is relatively anoxic and deprived of other nutrients. Repair therefore consists of an ingrowth of fibrous connective tissue and new blood vessels into the lesion. Even before the inflammatory response subsides, fibroblasts can be observed in the area. At first they are hard to distinguish by light microscopy from macrophages, but as they mature their true nature becomes clear. Because of their resemblance to large mononuclears, there has been a controversy as to whether they were derived from blood cells and emigrated out of the blood vessels or whether they migrated in from the surrounding normal tissue. This idea was favored by the appearance of similar cells capable of synthesizing collagen in tissue cultures derived from circulating blood. It appears, however, that these cells probably arose from connective tissue cells picked up by the needle going through layers of this tissue on its way into the blood ves-

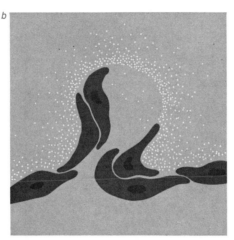

Figure 40:
New blood vessels form as the endothelial cells
at a budding site on an existing vessel
divide mitotically.
They slide past each other (a)
into positions distal from their place of origin (b).
The bud is formed (c)
and will then anastomose with other budding
vessels to make capillary loops.
The density of the surrounding tissue
may determine
the initial shape of the new vessels.

sel. R. Ross and J. W. Lillywhite found that when care was used to avoid this contamination, these collagen-producing cells did not occur in the cultures. Probably connective tissue cells in the surrounding tissue are awakened from their dormant state by something diffusing from the inflamed area. The cells seem to migrate along the strands of fibrin by amoeboid movement and distribute themselves through the healing area. They lose their oval configuration, become roughly stellate and finally elongate. During their development they acquire large complexes of rough endoplasmic reticulum and several Golgi complexes. Once they become fixed in a location, strands of collagen begin to appear about them (Fig 43). The amino acid proline, which together with hydroxyproline makes up about 20 per cent of collagen, can be given a radioactive tag. Radioautographs indicate that the amino acid is quickly taken up and almost immediately makes its way to the endoplasmic reticulum and soon thereafter is found outside the fibroblast again as collagen.

There are also a number of other experiments indicating that collagen is made in the endoplasmic reticulum and probably directly excreted. Other work indicates that glycoprotein is also made by the fibroblast. The protein part of this is synthesized in the endoplasmic reticulum and soon thereafter is transferred to the Golgi complex where the carbohydrate moiety is added.

For normal collagen to form, ascorbic acid is required. It was recognized in the 18th Century that when sailors developed scurvy their wounds would not heal and even some of their old wounds broke down. It was James Lind, late in the 18th century, who associated scurvy with a nutritional lack. S. B. Wolbach who made important studies of the pathology of scurvy observed that the fibroblasts of scorbutic guinea pigs produced a jelly-like material but were incapable of making mature collagen in typical fibrillar form. J. H. Crandon, who like Wolbach was at Harvard, produced scurvy in himself and confirmed the necessity of the vitamin in man for proper wound healing.

R. Ross and E. P. Benditt studied fibroblasts of both normal and scorbutic guinea pigs with the electron microscope. In the scorbutic animals they found marked changes in the endoplasmic reticulum which had broken down to form large vacuole-like structures. Furthermore, the ribosomes in normal animals were arranged in loose spirals *(Fig. 43-a);* in deficient animals this pattern was lost.

The vitamin C seems in some way needed for the conversion of proline and lysine to hydroxyproline and hydroxylysine respectively. Strangely this seems normally to occur after the collagen molecule has been almost completely formed in the endoplasmic reticulum. Both the structural change and the ability to form collagen can be quickly restored by supplying vitamin C.

The collagen fibers, laid down somewhat haphazardly at first, later form bundles oriented with their longitudinal axes in the direction of greatest stress *(Fig. 41).* As the collagen bundles become firm, the fibroblasts become atrophic and closely adhere to the bundles—now connective tissue cells. While the fibroblasts have been laying down collagen fibers, the macrophages have been cleaning up the evidences of inflammation.

The laying down of the new fibrous tissue requires both oxygen and nutrients. To supply this, new blood vessels grow into the relatively anoxic region. Just as some circumstances associated with the receding of the inflammatory process stimulate fibroblasts to invade the area, so the endothelium of the blood vessels in the area is stimulated to develop buds which elongate into new vessels and join with other developing vessels to form loops *(Fig. 42).*

As mitosis of endothelial cells occurs, the new cell forces itself between some of the existing cells, thus either increasing the diameter of the existing vessel or its length or both *(Fig. 40).* Eventually, one of the endothelial cells sends forth a pseudopod-like projection. The cell body then tends to follow the pseudopod, and the cell thus crawls away from the existing vessel but never loses contact with it. Soon other adjacent cells do likewise. In this way the more distant cells move away so as to make room for the new cells that are being formed by mitosis. The advancing cells may form more or less solid strands which subsequently develop a lumen or may form sac-like pouches that enlarge and elongate. As the vessels advance in this way, they may branch and usually meet other elongating trunks with which they fuse and form loops. The cells in the forefront of an invading vessel have no basement membrane and may not be too closely fitted together because they can be shown to have leaks which spill injected tracers directly into the tissue spaces. Soon, however, the cells fit tighter and a basement membrane develops.

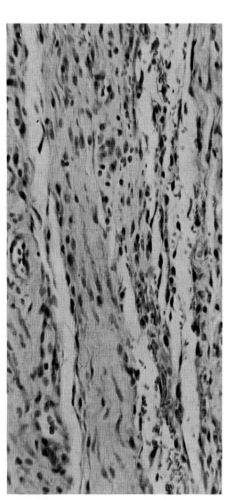

Figure 41:
Skeletal muscle in which connective tissue is being formed. Many fibroblasts are evident. The elongated dark shapes are their nuclei.

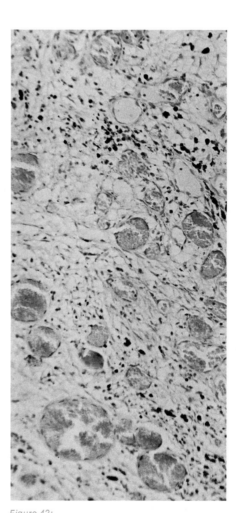

Figure 42:
A light micrograph of a section of dog heart shows a vascular bed in which new capillaries, transversely sectioned, are forming.

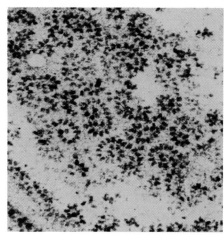

Figure 43a:
This enlarged detail of a section (blue square)
from the electron micrograph below
shows ribosomes in spiral arrangements,
probably assembled by messenger RNA
to synthesize chains of protein, presumably
tropocollagen.

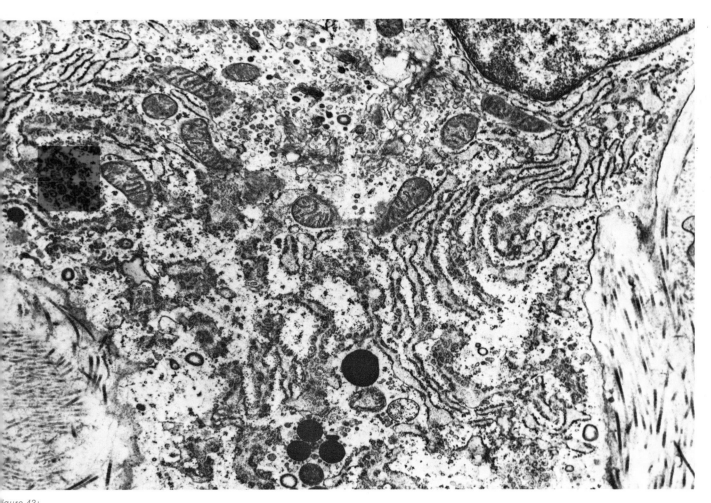

Figure 43:
An electron micrograph
of the cytoplasmic interior of a fibroblast
reveals much synthesizing activity,
indicated by extensive endoplasmic reticulum.
Outside the borders of the cell
(lower left and lower right)
are fibrils of newly synthesized tropocollagen.

As new vessels grow into a healing area, they bring nutrients and oxygen. Many too many vessels are usually produced to supply the needs of the highly cellular tissue. As the new-formed tissue matures, many of the new vessels atrophy and disappear as the blood supply becomes appropriately adjusted to the needs of the tissue.

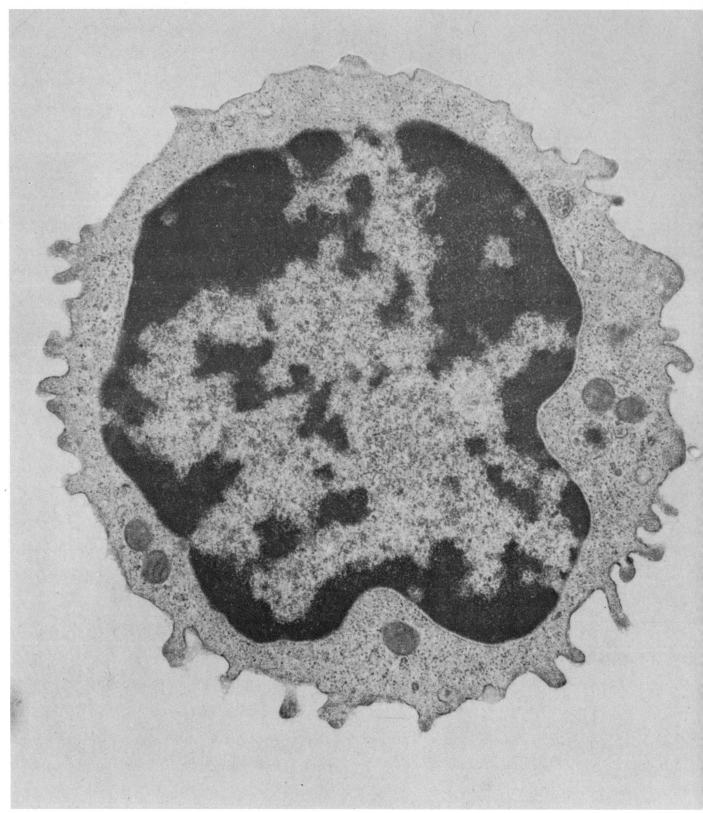

Figure 44:
An electron micrograph of a human lymphocyte.
The large nucleus, few granules,
and the villus-like processes at the cell border
are typical features.
The structural information needed
for antibody synthesis
appears to be picked up by lymphocytes
and transmitted to their daughter cells
when they divide.

Chronic inflammation

Chronic inflammation is a well recognized pathologic entity and there are many well characterized varieties of it. The pathologist consequently has no difficulty in recognizing the condition and is usually able to put it into an established category and associate the lesion with a clinical disease and may even be able to indicate the etiologic agent responsible. In other words, our empiric knowledge of the classifications of chronic inflammations is great, but our knowledge of their biochemistry particularly at the cell level is meager. For example, attempts to discover just what it is that determines the chronicity of a lesion have yielded no spectacular results. It seems more likely that it is the persistence of the irritating stimulus rather than some self-perpetuating factor in the inflammatory process itself. For example, in a granuloma, which is a typical chronic inflammation, there remains in the necrotic center some sort of invader that can not quite be killed or otherwise disposed of, e.g. tubercle bacilli, but which can be walled off and contained so that the lesion remains localized. The organism as a whole is protected, but the inflammatory stimulus still persists locally. Metchnikoff in his original work on phagocytosis mentions this protective walling off of an invader that could not be phagocytized (Fig. 46).

Some progress has, however, been made in working out how the cellular exudate in a chronic inflammation is maintained. By labeling blood cells with tritiated thymidine and colloidal carbon prior to injury, it was possible to determine that the mononuclear cells of the initial exudate came from the circulation. They were mostly monocytes. Few lymphocytes occurred in the early exudates. If the reaction resolves, the monocytes gradually disappear over a period of a few days. If the reaction persists, a change takes place in these cells; they enlarge, the amount of cytoplasm increases, the chromatin pattern of the nucleus changes, and it can be shown that DNA synthesis is taking place. Mitosis of these cells then occurs. From this point on, while some cells continue to migrate from the blood vessels, most of the mononuclears in the exudate are supplied by mitosis of those already there. This continues as long as the lesion lasts. Many of the small lymphocytes, which become an important part of the exudate as the process becomes chronic, are believed to arise by mitosis from larger mononuclears at the site. Calculations indicate that the turnover rate of the cells in the exudate is high. The cells needed to replace those lost by the high death rate are largely supplied by mitosis, although some continue to come from the blood vessels.

W. G. Spector's investigations indicate that at about 48 hours a turning point is reached. At this point, if enlargement of the mononuclears and DNA synthesis are evident in a large portion of the cells, the lesion is probably destined to be chronic. Otherwise, it is likely soon to start to regress.

One way to bring out some of the current concepts of chronic inflammation is to discuss the origin, function and fate of some of the cells that are found in these exudates.

Eosinophils

While the role of neutrophils in the inflammatory reaction is well defined, that of their close relatives the eosinophils has remained rather mysterious. Morphologically, the eosinophil in many ways resembles a neutrophil but its granules are much larger and somewhat more uniform in size. Electron microscopy reveals that many of these granules contain more or less rectangular inclusions which seem to be crystalline in structure. What the crystalline material is is not known.

Eosinophil granules have been analyzed and they contain an assortment of enzymes similar to those found in the neutrophils, except that they do not contain either lysozyme or phagocytin. These granules, therefore, meet the ordinary criteria for lysosomes.

Eosinophils move somewhat like neutrophils but more slowly and awkwardly. They are capable of phagocytosis. Hirsch, using time-lapse movies, has shown that they can phagocytize certain materials. He used in one case sensitized foreign red cells. The eosinophils phagocytized these in much the same manner that neutrophils engulf bacteria. As the phagosome formed and the red cell was pulled in, granules united with it and disappeared from the cytoplasm. Electron micrographs show a fusing of the eosinophil's lysosomes with the phagosome similar to that occurring in the neutrophil.

G. W. Thorn a number of years ago studied the reduction in the circulating eosinophils that occurred when adrenocortical hormones entered the bloodstream. The phenomenon has proved useful in the study of the cortical hormones but despite much work has not shed much light on the function of eosinophils.

For many years there has seemed to be an association between eosinophils and histamine. These possibilities existed: (1) histamine attracts eosinophils; (2) eosinophils contain an antihistamine material, or (3) eosinophils contain histamine. Satisfactory evidence that histamine attracts eosinophils has not been forthcoming. The possibility that the materials in the granules of the cell neutralized histamine has been investigated. Eventually material from the granules was prepared and tested against histamine. It did indeed have some slight neutralizing effect but it now appears that this is probably not an important function of the cell. Analysis of eosinophil granules has shown the presence of considerable amounts of histamine. But here again, there is no good evidence that the cell acts as a conveyor of histamine.

The idea advocated by Mortimer Litt that antigen-antibody complexes attract eosinophils has proved to be by far the most fruitful hypothesis so far advanced. On the assumption that this is the case, eosinophils seem to be in the right place at the right time. Such antigen-antibody complexes have a short half-life in the blood so that it is only where they are arrested at tissue sites or where they are constantly being produced that accumulations of eosinophils can be expected. For example, in infestations with parasites, the antigen because of its bulk persists for a long time. It is therefore available to unite with the host's antibodies. In chronic inflammations eosinophils are often prominent and are frequently seen in association with plasma cells. The presence of these latter cells indicates that abundant antibody is probably available. Litt has pointed out many situations where abundant antigen-antibody complexes can be demonstrated and where accumulations of eosinophils are characteristically found.

It therefore at present seems probable that an important if not the principal function of the eosinophils is to phagocytize antigen-antibody complexes and dispose of them. It certainly seems that the sites where the production of these is most likely—the lung, the skin, and gastrointestinal tract—are the tissues richest in eosinophils.

While the neutrophils also phagocytize antigen-antibody complexes, it is possible that eosinophils do so more efficiently. While antigen-antibody complexes seem the most effective attractants of eosinophils, they are probably not the only ones; the eosinophil undoubtedly has a number of important functions.

The lymphocyte

In an earlier part of this essay mention has already been made of the small mononuclear or lymphocyte. The cell is familiar to both the hematologist and pathologist and forms part of the cellular exudate of almost all inflammatory reactions if they are of more than the briefest duration. It is by far the most numerous of the cells of the lymphoid series. For years lymphocytes were thought to arise from stem cells in lymphoid tissue which in turn had arisen from reticulum cells. Because the thymus is definitely necessary for the normal development of lymphocytes and the lymphatic system, i has been proposed that it was the original source of lymphocytes and that the lymphoblasts or stem cells were all descendents of cells emanating from the thymus. However this may be, lymphocytes can also develop from other lymphocytes. They are long-lived cells, surviving in excess of 90 days and possibly as long as a year.

Lymphocytes are always present in the blood but are also constantly found in lymph nodes, lymphatic tissue, lymphatics and the thoracic duct. It has been demonstrated that lymphocytes circulate over a much more complicated route than other blood cells. When travelling with the blood, they arrive at the post-capillary venules of a lymph node or other lymphoid tissue and there may leave the bloodstream by burrowing through the cytoplasm of the endothelial cells. The venules from which they escape are found in the cortex of lymph nodes and have a particularly thick endothelium. Lymphocytes are frequently found completely within the cytoplasm of these cells. After gaining entrance to the parenchyma of the lymph node, they travel by lymphatic vessels perhaps to other lymph nodes but eventually re-enter the bloodstream through a lymphatic or the thoracic duct.

Ordinarily lymphocytes when examined by electron microscopy show few organelles (Fig. 44), usually only a few mitochondria and some granules. A slightly larger variety may contain prominent Golgi complexes in addition, and a still further variety contain a well developed endoplasmic reticulum. It is thought that those in this latter group divide to produce small lymphocytes. In human beings even some small lymphocytes may contain some endoplasmic reticulum.

There has been much controversy about whether on the one hand lymphocytes are end cells and incapable of reproduction or transformation, or, on the other hand are able to develop into macrophages, fibroblasts or stem cells. Recent studies do not support the idea that lymphocytes can be transformed into macrophages, fibroblasts or stem cells. Nevertheless, it has been shown that they can develop into large pyroninophilic cells which are capable of dividing.

Although lymphocytes are incapable of phagocytosis, they are not without utility in defense against infection, because they are deeply concerned with the development of immunity. This has been demonstrated in various ways. For example, the primary antibody response becomes greatly depressed in an animal most of whose small lymphocytes have been removed by drainage of the thoracic duct. The response can be restored if the animal is injected with a 99 per cent pure suspension of small lymphocytes. How the lymphocyte is involved in the production of antibodies, however, still remains in doubt but it seems to be the cell that picks up the necessary structural information about the antigen for the formation of the antibody. After a lymphocyte has picked up this information it can transmit it to its daughter cells when it divides. This is an important means of increasing antibody production. Once a lymphocyte is committed to a particular antigen it is usually not available to react to another one, although a few cells seem capable of producing antibodies to two antigens. At any one time, therefore, only the uncommitted lymphocytes are available to react with new antigen. Although lymphocytes are not as great producers of antibody as plasma cells, they are, nevertheless, capable of producing it.

Plasma cell

Another cell often seen in inflammatory exudates particularly when inflammation has become chronic is the plasma cell. There is little doubt that the plasma cells, acting on information somehow transmitted from the lymphocytes, are the principal sources of antibodies which are generated in their endoplasmic reticulum. The most conspicuous feature of the plasma cell is the large amount of rough endoplasmic reticulum with which the cytoplasm is crowded. The cell also contains conspicuous Golgi complexes. Antibody has been demonstrated in the endoplasmic reticulum; (Fig. 45) whether it is secreted directly from this organelle after formation or is first transmitted to the Golgi complex is not clear.

Plasma cells usually arise in lymph nodes or spleen but from what precursors is controversial. Some experiments seem to indicate that they arise from stem cells in these organs, others that they might arise in some way from small lymphocytes. If the latter is the case, the method whereby the information concerning the antigen is transferred from the lymphocyte ceases to be a problem. Clearly they arise as needed from some cell of the lymphoid series. They are not themselves capable of reproduction.

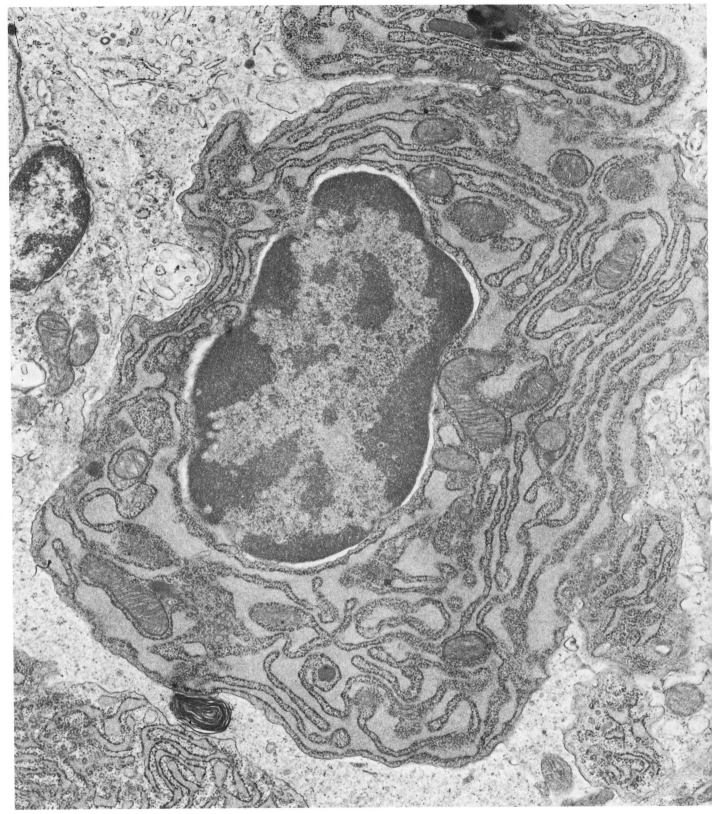

Figure 45:
A plasma cell from a rat intestine
shows a large amount of rough endoplasmic
reticulum, with conspicuous ribosomes.
The nucleus displays a characteristic arrangement
of chromatin,
with electron dense masses around the perimeter.

Anti-inflammatory agents

Any discussion of inflammation would be incomplete without some mention of anti-inflammatory agents, particularly those types that have proved useful clinically. Obviously the most satisfactory means of treating an inflammatory disease is to eliminate its cause. Consequently, in one sense the most effective anti-inflammatory agents of modern times have been the antimicrobial agents such as the sulfa drugs and antibiotics. There still remain, however, those inflammatory conditions which are noninfectious, notably the so-called collagen diseases.

Histamine early attracted attention as a possible mediator of the inflammatory reaction, so much research was directed toward finding a specific antagonist for it. As a result, a number of highly effective antagonists have been developed. They have proved very useful for the control of certain manifestations of allergy and other conditions. Even though their undesired side effects have not been serious, the high hopes originally held for them have not been realized, not because they did not effectively neutralize the effect of histamine but because antagonizing it was not tantamount to antagonizing inflammation. Not the least of the advantages of their discovery has been in defining more accurately the role of histamine in inflammation.

Another group of drugs used empirically for the control of inflammation and pain for many years are the salicylates. Some mention of their antagonism to certain mediators of inflammation has already been made, but a completely satisfactory explanation of their mode of action has still to be found.

The so-called acidic drugs, such as phenylbutazone and indomethacin, are another group of anti-inflammatory drugs of clinical importance. These drugs *in vitro* inhibit the release of lactic dehydrogenases and acid phosphatase from platelets, and inhibit hypotonic and hyperthermic lysis of erythrocytes. But since these effects do not parallel their anti-inflammatory efficacy they cannot satisfactorily explain their action.

Corticosteroids and inflammation

The adrenal corticosteroids are among the most potent anti-inflammatory agents yet discovered, and they are effective almost regardless of the cause of inflammation. Soon after P. S. Hench's discovery of the remarkable antirheumatic effect of cortisone, it was discovered that the dramatic relief afforded patients with rheumatoid arthritis was attributable to cortisone's general anti-inflammatory effect rather than to any specific action against the disease itself. Likewise, in other diseases whose symptoms were controlled by cortisone, it was found that the drug's action was to alleviate the inflammatory component.

This ability to combat inflammation has made the corticosteroids immensely useful but also potentially harmful. Where inflammations are protective as in many infections, inhibiting the response may prove dangerous. It is for this reason that the corticosteroids have their greatest usefulness in sterile inflammations.

Organic chemists have made many modifications of the corticosteroid molecule that have intensified certain actions and minimized others. For example, W. E. Dulin and associates found that 6-methylation of a number of C_{21} steroids increased glucocorticoid activity and decreased salt-retaining activity. The most biologically potent synthetic compounds are those in which the basic hydrocortisone structure is modified to protect it from degradation by metabolic processes. Since it was found that anti-inflammatory activity like the glycogen deposition activity seemed dependent on the presence of hydroxyl groups on carbons 17 and 11 of the steroid molecule, modifications were designed to preserve these structures while protecting the molecule from metabolic degradation. It has been found that increasing the half-life of a compound correspondingly increases its activity.

While cortisone, the steroid that most of the early work in alleviating inflammation was done with, is not present in large amounts in the secretion of the adrenals, it is clear that the cortical secretion is indeed anti-inflammatory because ACTH, whose primary action is to stimulate its production is a potent anti-inflammatory agent. Likewise, adrenalectomized animals show greater reactions to inflammatory stimuli than normal animals. And finally, hydrocortisone which is a major component of cortical secretion is an even more satisfactory anti-inflammatory agent than cortisone. In fact, it has turned out that cortisone is activated in the body by being converted to hydrocortisone.

Glucocorticoids unlike some other anti-inflammatory agents are effective topically. When injected into loci of inflammation produced by burns, pyrogens, wounds, bacteria, antigen, etc. they reduce or inhibit the response.

Reduction of permeability

To further define the mode of action of the corticosteroids, their effects on the various components of the inflammatory response have been studied.

Valy Menkin (1940) early demonstrated that adrenal cortex extract applied locally reduced the extravasation of dye from small blood vessels made permeable by the application of inflammatory exudates. Subsequently he showed that cortisone had the same effect. This has subsequently been demonstrated in greater detail by R. H. Ebert and W. R. Barclay who showed a reduction in the leakage of both edema fluid and plasma protein. The inhibition by corticosteroids of the formation of kinins mentioned earlier is a possible factor in this response.

Sticking and migration of leucocytes

Several techniques have been used to evaluate the effect of corticosteroids on the number and type of leucocytes appearing at the inflammatory site after the induction of inflammation by various means. Using the rabbit ear chamber which permits observation of change occurring during inflammation, F. Allison Jr., M. B. Smith and W. B. Wood found that pretreatment with cortisone delayed the sticking of leucocytes to the endothelium and thereby their diapedesis.

Glucocorticoids also reduce the number of leucocytes in the exudate at the inflammatory site. As much as a four- to 10-fold decrease in the number has been observed in human volunteers using a skin-window technique. This reduction occurs despite the fact that neutrophils in the blood may be elevated at the time. A single intravenous dose of hydrocortisone, moreover, decreased the cellular response to an inflammatory stimulus which had been administered as much as eight hours later.

The effect of these drugs on neutrophil accumulation is greatest when they are applied locally. For example, it was found that a subcutaneous dose of 50 to 100 mg./kilogram of hydrocortisone was required to appreciably reduce neutrophil accumulation following intraperitoneal pyrogen injection whereas as little as 1 mg. administered intraperitoneally reduced the number of neutrophils to half the control value.

Chemotaxis and phagocytosis

P. A. Ward has studied the effects of corticosteroids on chemotaxis as measured in a simple chamber whose two compartments are separated by a micropore filter (pore size 650 $m\mu$). A suspension of rabbit polymorphonuclears was placed in the upper chamber and highly chemotactic material obtained by incubating rabbit serum with an antigen-antibody complex in the lower. He found that relatively low concentrations of hydrocortisone and methylprednisolone inhibited migration of the leucocytes to the lower chamber. The effect was not reversible by washing the leucocytes after their exposure to the drugs. He was also able to demonstrate that hydrocortisone prevented the accumulation of polymorphonuclears at a site of immunologic vasculitis produced by the reversed passive Arthus reaction. In both experiments he was able to rule out the effect of the drug on complement.

Ward also found that hydrocortisone and methylprednisolone reduced the leucocyte's ability to phagocytize zymosan granules, but relatively high concentrations of the drugs were required.

M. B. Lurie, studying the effect of cortisone in tuberculosis, found that the bacilli were phagocytized avidly by the macrophages but that they accumulated within the cell and were not digested

Steroids have been reported to have a similar effect on the digestion of pneumococci, streptococci and red blood cells. On the other hand, F. Allison and M. H. Adcock found that leucocytes from healthy human donors given 10 mg. of prednisolone orally every six hours for three days showed no diminution in their ability to phagocytize and kill Type I pneumococci.

Lysosomes

The concept that corticosteroids might stabilize the lysosomal membrane is an attractive one. To the extent that the disruption of lysosomes destroys tissue and intensifies the inflammatory response, steroids could by this means relieve such intensification. Also the failure of phagocytized bacteria to be killed and digested as described earlier could be accounted for by the drug's preventing the rupture

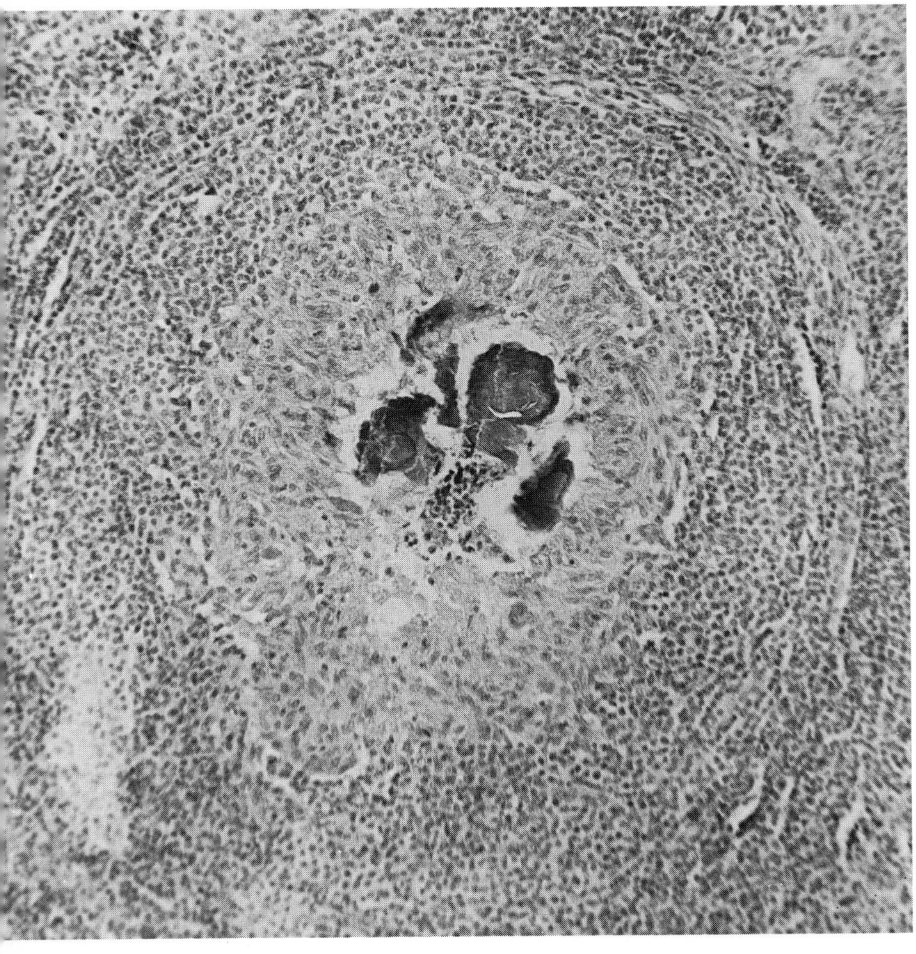

Figure 46:
A typical early granuloma from the lymph node of a dog.
The inflammatory cells are disposed in circular zones around the necrotic center.

of lysosomes. G. Weissmann and J. T. Dingle have prepared lysosomes from the livers of rats pretreated with cortisone and shown that their fragility to ultraviolet light is indeed reduced. Corticosteroids also protect against the damaging effects of other agents that have a rupturing effect on lysosomes such as thermal stress, excess oxygen, carbon

tetrachloride, endotoxins, traumatic shock and streptolysin O.

If phagocytosis of antigen and subsequent digestion with lysosomal enzymes are necessary steps in the production of antibody, stabilization of lysosomal membranes could also account for delay or failure in the development of immunity.

Lymphoid tissue and immunity

It has long been recognized that prolonged administration of corticosteroids can cause involution of lymphoid tissue and a reduction in the number of circulating lymphocytes. Since these are the tissues involved with antibody synthesis, steroid administration might be expected to affect it adversely. In experimental animals it has been possible to demonstrate interference with antibody production by treatment with glucocorticoids. The extent of this effect depends on both the dose of corticoid used and the amount of antigen administered. When larger doses of antigen are used, more corticoid is required to suppress the response. The glucocorticoids are most effective in suppressing an antibody response when they are given before immunization is started and continued throughout the process. Their greatest effect seems to be on the early stages of the process because they are relatively ineffective when administered after immunization is well under way. It may be they affect the processing of the antigen in phagocytic cells, or the multiplication of sensitized lymphoid cells—either blast cells in lymphoid tissue or lymphocytes. It appears that small lymphocytes when sensitized can divide and produce antibody and possibly become plasma cells. It was also shown that in a hyperimmune rabbit, cortisone reduced the rate at which isotopic glycine was incorporated into antibody but did not affect the rate at which it was utilized to make plasma protein.

The inhibitory effects of glucocorticoids on antibody production in rats, mice and rabbits have not been seen in primates. When rhesus monkeys received doses comparable to those that suppressed antibody production in mice (50 mg./kg.), the production of antibodies was not suppressed. A number of studies indicate that the response to immunization in man does not appear to be altered by cortisone, hydrocortisone or corticotropin treatment; gamma globulin synthesis is not affected.

The beneficial effects of the glucocorticoids on allergic manifestations in patients must therefore be attributed to the alleviation of the specific inflammation caused by the antigen-antibody reaction rather than to interference with the immune response itself.

Fibroblasts and collagen production

Controlled studies indicate that wound healing is delayed in patients receiving full therapeutic doses of glucocorticoids. A recent report indicates that steroid-treated patients require 16 days for the same degree of wound healing seen on the ninth day in patients not receiving steroids. This is apparently the result of impairment in the proliferation of fibroblasts and to decreased mature collagen production in the individual cell. There is probably also decreased production of mucopolysaccharides. For example, human fibroblasts incubated with 10 μg./ml. of hydrocortisone produced less hyaluronic acid than control cells did.

It has also been observed that proliferation of blood vessels in the injured area is reduced in experimental animals receiving glucocorticoids.

In summary it appears that hydrocortisone and related glucocorticoids exert their anti-inflammatory effect by direct action on the participating cells, but there is as yet no precise information as to where and how within the cell this influence is exerted. A possible exception is in the case of lysosomes, if their effect on the membranes on these organelles is direct and physical. In any case, lysosomal stabilization does not account for all the effects observed. There is, however work that seems to be leading toward a more fundamental understanding of the action of these drugs. E. Myles Glenn and his associates have extensively studied the metabolic effects of a large number of glucocorticoids and have found a close relationship to always exist between their anti-inflammatory potency and their ability to inhibit the oxidation of glucose and to promote glycogen synthesis. This and other observations made by the same group suggest that the inflammatory reaction is suppressed because the participating cells are deprived of the energy necessary to perform their appointed tasks.

It was suggested early in this essay that inflammation is the means whereby an organism can divert part of its energy for defense. If the glucocorticoids obstruct this diversion, they are useful only when the defense is unnecessary or temporarily ill-advised.

The Upjohn Company gratefully acknowledges the advice, information, and illustrative material contributed by the following scientists for the monograph and exhibit, "Defense of Life."

Ramzi S. Cotran
*Mallory Institute of Pathology,
Boston City Hospital, Boston, Mass.
(Figs. 18, 20, 26, 44)*

Don W. Fawcett
*Department of Anatomy,
Harvard Medical School, Boston, Mass.
(Fig. 8)*

Lester Grant
*Department of Medicine,
New York University Medical Center
New York, N.Y.*

James G. Hirsch
*Rockefeller University,
New York, N.Y.
and
Academic Press
The Inflammatory Process, 1965,
Eds. Zweifach, Grant and McCluskey.
(Fig. 31)*

J. C. Houck
*Biochemical Research Laboratories,
Children's Hospital, Washington, D.C.*

Morris J. Karnovsky
*Department of Pathology,
Harvard Medical School, Boston, Mass.
and
Rockefeller University Press,
Journal of Cell Biology, Vol. 35, 1967.
(Fig. 15)*

Toichiro Kuwabara
*Howe Laboratory of Ophthalmology,
Massachusetts Eye and Ear Infirmary,
Boston, Mass.
(Fig. 47)*

John H. Luft
*Department of Biological Structure,
University of Washington,
School of Medicine, Seattle, Wash.
and
Academic Press
The Inflammatory Process, 1965.
(Figs. 9-11)
and
American Society for Experimental Biology,
Federation Proceedings, Vol. 25, 1966.
(Figs. 12-14)*

R. C. Macfarlane
*Blood Coagulation Research Unit,
The Churchill Hospital,
Oxford, England
and
Academic Press,
The Inflammatory Process, 1965.
(Fig. 38)*

Guido Majno
*Institut de Pathologie de l'Université,
Geneva, Switzerland*

Vincent T. Marchesi
*Section of Chemical Pathology,
National Institutes of Health, Bethesda, Md.
(Figs. 23-25)*

Keith Porter
*Department of Biology,
Harvard University, Cambridge, Mass.
(Figs. 17,45)*

Russell Ross and Earl P. Benditt
*Department of Pathology,
University of Washington,
School of Medicine, Seattle, Wash.
and
Rockefeller University Press,
Journal of Cell Biology, Vol.22,1964.
(Fig. 43)*

Alexander Tomasz
*Rockefeller University,
New York, N.Y.*

Gerald Weissmann
*Department of Medicine,
New York University Medical Center
New York, N.Y.*

Sumner Wood, Jr.
*Department of Pathology,
Johns Hopkins University,
School of Medicine,
Baltimore, Md.*

Dorothea Zucker-Franklin
*Department of Medicine,
New York University Medical Center,
New York, N.Y.
(Figs. 33, 34, 36)*

Benjamin W. Zweifach
*Department of Aerospace and Mechanical
Engineering, University of California,
La Jolla, Cal.*

National Library of Medicine
*Bethesda, Md.
(Figs. 1-6)*

The Upjohn Company
*Pathology and Toxicology Research
(Figs. 41, 42, 46)*

Color photographs *By Ezra Stoller,
Mamaroneck, N.Y.
from the exhibit "Defense of Life"*

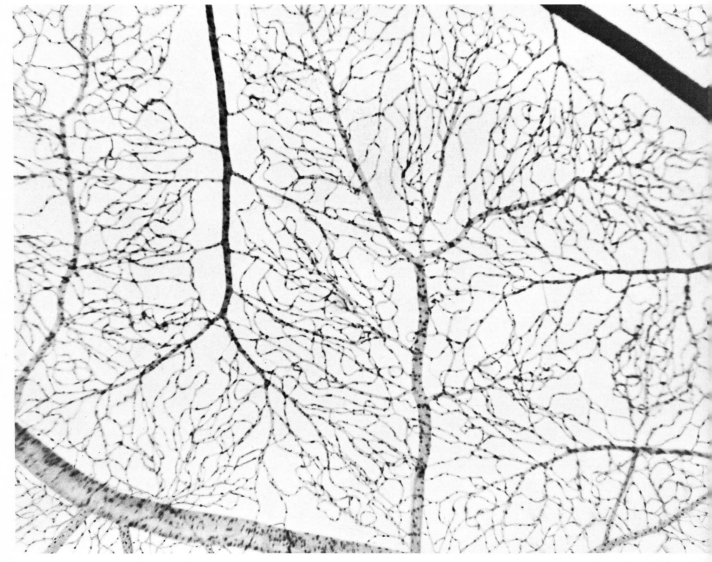

Figure 47:

This photomicrograph is of a vascular network
in the human retina. The dark vessel in the
upper right hand corner is an arteriole,
that in the opposite corner is a venule.